Grade 4

Scott Foresman

Fresh Reads
for Differentiated Test Practice

D1211530

PEARSON

Scott Foresman

Editorial Offices: Glenview, Illinois • Parsippany, New Jersey • New York, New York
Sales Offices: Needham, Massachusetts • Duluth, Georgia • Glenview, Illinois
Coppell, Texas • Sacramento, California • Mesa, Arizona

ISBN: 0-328-16980-3

6 7 8 9 10 V004 14 13 12 11 10 09 08

Contents

Fresh Reads

Read the selection. Then answer the questions that follow.

Beach Party

Deb shook the crumbs off her beach towel and started off across the sandy beach to the lake. A strong wind was blowing, and the sun had disappeared behind black clouds. Very exciting weather, Deb thought.

"Where do you think you're going?" asked her mother, who was busy filling a beach bag. "That storm is coming in fast."

"Oh, Mom," said Deb. "Let's just stay till it starts to rain."

"No way," said her mother. "This is a dangerous place to be in a storm. Don't you know that lightning is attracted to water?"

Reluctantly Deb turned back. Quickly they finished packing and then carried everything to the car. Suddenly a flash of lightning lit up the sky, followed immediately by a crash of thunder. Rain began to fall in big fat drops that came faster and faster.

"Just in time," said Deb.

Turn the page.

Answer the questions below.

1 What did Deb do right before her mother said, "Where do you think you're going"?

  A carried their things to the car

  B said, "Just in time"

  C walked toward the lake

  D shook the crumbs out of her beach towel

2 Which of these events happened last in this story?

  F The clouds covered the sun.

  G It began to rain.

  H There was a crash of thunder.

  J There was a flash of lightning.

3 Why did the author end the story with the words "Just in time"?

  A to make it clear that Deb obeyed her mother

  B to remind the reader that time is important

  C to show that Deb was safely in the car

  D to point out the moral of the story

4 How did Deb's mother know that a storm was coming? Use sequence words in your answer.

_____

_____

_____

_____

_____

_____

_____

_____

_____

_____

Read the selection. Then answer the questions that follow.

Flapjacks

You may know them as flapjacks. But they go by other names as well, including griddle cakes and hot cakes. The name depends on where you live. Still, most Americans know a pancake when they see one.

This all-American food is delicious and easy to make. You can whip up a batter in a matter of minutes. All you need is milk, an egg, butter, flour, baking powder, and oil.

First, mix a tablespoon of baking powder with a half cup of flour. Next beat together the egg with a half cup of milk and a quarter cup of oil. Slowly mix the dry ingredients with the wet ones.

Now your batter is ready. Heat up a large frying pan and add two tablespoons of butter. Pour spoonfuls of batter into the melted butter. Let the pancakes fry until they are golden brown on the bottom. Flip them over and brown them on the other side. Serve the pancakes hot with maple syrup, honey, or jam.

This simple recipe has many variations. Some people use buttermilk instead of milk. Others use yogurt mixed with milk. Some cooks mix whole wheat, cornmeal, or oats into the flour. Of course, choices for pancake toppings are endless. Fruit, chocolate, and whipped cream are just a few favorites.

How do you like your hot cakes?

Turn the page.

Answer the questions below.

1 **What do you do after you mix the egg, milk, and oil?**

  A pour batter into the frying pan

  B mix dry and wet ingredients

  C add butter to the frying pan

  D add buttermilk to the mix

2 **For cornmeal pancakes, when should you add the cornmeal?**

  F after you heat the frying pan

  G after you add the toppings

  H when you mix the wet ingredients

  J when you mix the dry ingredients

3 **What happens right after you add butter to the frying pan?**

  A You add the flour.

  B You serve the pancakes.

  C The butter melts.

  D Pancake toppings are endless.

4 **The author probably wrote this selection to**

  F explain how to make pancakes.

  G convince the reader that pancakes are great for breakfast.

  H entertain the reader with an interesting story about pancakes.

  J express strong feelings about pancakes.

5 **List the three main things you have to do to make pancakes. Use sequence words in your answer.**

_____

_____

_____

_____

_____

_____

_____

Read the selection. Then answer the questions that follow.

Missing Dog

Barry raced into the house, forgetting to close the back door. He was late for his baseball game and not thinking about his mother's warning about keeping that door closed so that Happy couldn't push it open and escape.

Barry changed into his uniform and grabbed his mitt. He was about to leave the house when he realized that he hadn't seen Happy. At the same instant, Barry noticed that the door was not quite closed. He called for the dog, but Happy did not appear. He checked the entire house, but the mutt had vanished. If anything happened to that dog, Barry thought, he would not forgive himself, and nobody else in the family would either.

Barry spent the next hour searching the neighborhood for Happy. He asked all his neighbors the same question: "Have you seen a little black-and-white mutt with big paws and enormous ears that is really friendly?"

They all shook their heads sympathetically.

Barry had just started designing a LOST DOG poster when his mother's car pulled into the driveway. He jogged over to her and was about to announce the bad news, when he caught sight of Happy sitting in the backseat. His mother rolled down the window and said, "Aren't you supposed to be at the baseball game?"

Turn the page.

Answer the questions below.

1 What happened before the events described in this story took place?

  A Barry played in a ball game.

  B Barry's mother let the dog out the back door.

  C Barry changed into his uniform and grabbed his mitt.

  D Barry's mother warned him to keep the back door closed.

2 What happened right after Barry came into the house?

  F He noticed that Happy was missing.

  G He changed into his uniform.

  H His mother took the dog with her.

  J He shouted for the dog.

3 Why did Barry look for Happy in the house first?

  A Happy was supposed to be in the house.

  B He knew that Happy had not left the house.

  C He did not have time to search the neighborhood.

  D Happy could open the back door.

4 What information did the author hold back in order to have a surprise ending?

_____

_____

_____

_____

_____

5 At the end of the story, what did Barry probably do next?

_____

_____

_____

_____

_____

_____

Read the selection. Then answer the questions that follow.

Rabbit Fools Coyote

Coyote was hiding behind a bush waiting for Rabbit to leave his hole. But Rabbit was no fool. He knew just where Coyote was hiding and what he would probably be up to.

One day when Rabbit left his hole, he carried a big bag and pretended that he had to run slowly because the bag was so heavy. Soon Coyote overtook him.

"Before you eat me, please let me empty my bag," Rabbit said. "My children are all sleeping inside."

Coyote laughed and grabbed the bag while Rabbit raced away. Coyote sat down, looking forward to the delicious meal in the bag. He stuck his head and front paws inside and, "YEOW!" yelled out Coyote. The bag was full of thorny cactuses.

Turn the page.

Answer the questions below.

1 Why do you think the author wrote this story?

  A to convince the reader of an opinion

  B to entertain the reader with a surprise ending

  C to explain how to act in an emergency

  D to express a feeling and create a mood

2 What did the author probably want you to think about Coyote?

  F He was very clever.

  G He got what he deserved.

  H He should not have chased Rabbit.

  J He was too proud of himself.

3 Why did Rabbit say his children were sleeping in the bag?

  A He wanted Coyote to leave them alone.

  B He wanted to show them to Coyote.

  C He wanted Coyote to be quiet.

  D He wanted to trick Coyote.

4 Do you think the author was trying to make you laugh? Explain by giving an example from the story.

_____

_____

_____

_____

_____

_____

_____

_____

_____

_____

Read the selection. Then answer the questions that follow.

Letter from a New Home

September 5

Dear Nadja,

I've put away my things in my new room, and my posters are on the walls. Now this is starting to feel like home.

I can see the mountains and lots of pine trees from my window. My mom says I can take skiing lessons this winter, so I can't wait for the snow. There are a zillion places to go ice skating and tobogganing. Who knows, maybe I'll even learn to snowboard!

Yesterday we hiked up a mountain path that led to a beautiful lookout. The land stretched out for miles and miles across a canyon. Hawks were drifting in the sky, and it was almost like a dream. My dad had brought a picnic, and we ate lunch there. It was warm in the sun. By the time we got back to the car, I was tired and cold and my muscles ached, but I slept well last night.

School starts on Monday, and I'm a little nervous about being the "new kid" here. I just hope my teachers are nice and that I make some friends fast. If I could just change one thing here, can you guess what it would be? You got it—you would still live next door.

Your friend,

Rosa

P.S. Write back soon! You know how I love to get mail.

Turn the page.

Answer the questions below.

1 **Why do you think the author wrote this selection?**

 A to persuade the reader to move to the mountains

 B to entertain the reader with interesting facts

 C to describe what it's like to be in a new home

 D to explain why hiking is a great sport

2 **In the paragraph that begins "School starts on Monday," the author's purpose is mainly to**

 F give information.

 G ask a question.

 H describe a place.

 J express feelings.

3 **The author's purpose in the first part of the letter is to show that Rosa**

 A misses her friend.

 B is getting used to a new home.

 C is sorry that she moved away.

 D likes to ski.

4 **What caused Rosa to sleep so well the night before she wrote?**

 F unpacking

 G hiking

 H skiing

 J feeling happy

5 **Why do you think the author chose to write about moving to a new home?**

_____

_____

_____

_____

_____

_____

_____

Read the selection. Then answer the questions that follow.

Tornadoes Strike Three States

Friday, August 15

Last night a string of tornadoes cut a thousand-mile path across Kansas, Oklahoma, and Texas. The National Weather Service reported that in some areas, winds reached 180 miles an hour.

Today, businesses were shut down across the three states. Trees and telephone poles were uprooted. Power lines were down. Many areas are expected to be without electricity or gas for several days.

Early yesterday evening, the weather service put out storm warnings. A strong warm front was expected to meet a strong cold front, leading to as many as ten separate tornadoes as well as huge downpours.

Many area residents were shaking their heads today. "I looked out the picture window at sunset and saw two twisters coming my way," recalled Mabel Brown. "I just grabbed my cats and raced for the cellar."

As it turned out, the storm bypassed Mrs. Brown's home, but she could hear trees cracking and glass crashing. She sat under a table with her pets for what seemed like hours, she thought. Actually it was just a few minutes.

When the tornado had passed, Mrs. Brown said, "The neighborhood was a mess. Still, I'm grateful that everyone is safe, and their houses are all standing. On the whole we were very, very lucky."

Turn the page.

Answer the questions below.

1 What is the author's main purpose in this selection?

A to entertain the reader

B to inform the reader with the latest news

C to warn the reader about tornadoes

D to tell the reader how to survive a tornado

2 Which of the following does the author use most to make the selection informative?

F short paragraphs and varied information

G technical terms and scientific information

H weather facts and historical information

J complex paragraphs and geographic information

3 What was the author's main purpose in writing the paragraph that begins "Early yesterday evening"?

A to catch the reader's attention

B to explain the cause of the tornadoes

C to describe the area after the tornado

D to list problems the tornadoes caused

4 Why did Mrs. Brown feel as if she had been in the basement for hours instead of minutes?

_____

_____

_____

_____

_____

5 Give one reason why you think the author quoted Mabel Brown.

_____

_____

_____

_____

_____

Read the selection. Then answer the questions that follow.

Wish Comes True

Dear Diary,

When I went to bed last night, I made a wish. When I woke up this morning, I saw that my wish had come true. A blanket of snow covered the ground.

Mom fixed me pancakes before I put on my warmest coat, gloves, and boots. I met Lisa at Cobb Hill with my sled.

Sledding down Cobb Hill is more fun than any ride at the amusement park. I love coasting down with the wind in my face and the sun on my back. It's a long trek back up, but it's worth it!

After we'd been sledding awhile, we met up with Nan and Betty. They had a toboggan, and we all went down together.

Turn the page.

Answer the questions below.

1 Which of these events happened last?

  A meeting Lisa

  B meeting Nan and Betty

  C going to Cobb Hill

  D sledding down Cobb Hill

2 Which of these events happened before the writer woke up?

  F Her mom gave her pancakes.

  G Her wish came true.

  H She met her friends.

  J She put on her warmest coat.

3 What is the main idea of the third paragraph?

  A Amusement parks are not very much fun.

  B The day at Cobb Hill was windy and sunny.

  C Sledding down Cobb Hill was a lot of fun.

  D Cobb Hill was a long slope and hard to climb.

4 How would you get dressed to go sledding? Use sequence words in your answer.

_____

_____

_____

_____

_____

_____

_____

_____

_____

_____

_____

_____

Read the selection. Then answer the questions that follow.

Topeka Tess

No doubt you have heard tales of Pecos Bill and Paul Bunyan. The feats of Topeka Tess are not so famous, not yet. Even so, there are people who brag about her out on the Great Plains of these great United States.

Tess was born in farm country. In fact, her birthday fell right in the middle of the biggest harvest of all times.

Tess came into this world like all babies, crying. However, her crying was different. It was more like talking. "Please, oh please, Mama," she bawled. "Let me help Papa in the fields!" When her ma said she couldn't because she was too little, Topeka Tess let out a shout that could be heard from Kansas to Ohio.

When Tess turned two, she was harvesting her family's fields all by herself. At ten, she mowed every field in Kansas.

By the age of fifteen, Tess was ready for her biggest challenge ever. One afternoon, Tess's father got a call from a neighbor. Trouble was brewing. A giant swarm of locusts was heading their way, gobbling up crops as they flew.

Tess set to work weaving a net. Then she waited for the swarm. When it arrived, she trapped every last locust in her net. Better yet, she used the wing power of those bugs to help her mow the fields. Is it any wonder Topeka Tess is the hero of America's heartland?

© Pearson Education 4

Turn the page.

Answer the questions below.

1 When Tess was born, what was the first thing she did?

   A let out a shout that could be heard for miles

   B harvested her family's fields all by herself

   C cried until her mother picked her up

   D begged to help her father in the fields

2 What did Tess have to do before she could catch the locusts?

   F weave a net to trap them

   G harvest her family's fields

   H mow every field in Kansas

   J use the locusts to mow the fields

3 What would a field of corn look like after the locusts passed by?

   A The corn would be stacked into piles.

   B The field would be covered with a net.

   C The corn would be waving in the wind.

   D No corn would be left in the field.

4 What is the main idea of the last paragraph?

   F Tess saved the crops by trapping the locusts.

   G Tess was amazing at weaving nets.

   H Tess could mow a field using locusts.

   J Tess was faster than anyone on Earth.

5 What three important events took place in the selection and when did they occur? Use sequence words in your answer.

_____

_____

_____

_____

_____

_____

_____

Read the selection. Then answer the questions that follow.

Subway Ride

Jen followed Nicky and her mother down a flight of stairs. Nicky's mother handed Jen a token. Jen slipped the coin into a slot and pushed through the turnstile. Then they all went down another flight of stairs and onto the subway platform.

Jen heard a rumbling that sounded like an earthquake. She was bracing for the walls to start shaking, when a train roared into the station. It screeched to a stop in front of them. There was a crowd waiting to get on the train. Jen, Nicky, and Nicky's mother got on with them.

The seats filled up before Jen or Nicky could sit down. "Hang on to that bar," said Nicky's mother, and Jen held on for dear life. The train began to speed up and then entered a dark tunnel. Nicky said something to Jen, but she could not hear a word over the rumbling of the train.

After a minute, the train came to another screeching halt. "Six more stops to the aquarium," Nicky said.

By the time the train reached the aquarium stop, Jen was used to the noise and the motion of the train. In fact, she had found her first ride on a Boston subway train very exciting. She just hoped their trip to the aquarium would be as much fun.

Turn the page.

Answer the questions below.

1 What did Jen do right after she slipped the token into the slot?

   A braced for the tunnel walls to shake

   B went down a flight of stairs

   C held on for dear life

   D pushed through the turnstile

2 What is the first paragraph mostly about?

   F riding on a subway train for the first time

   G going from the street to the subway tunnel

   H taking the subway to the aquarium in Boston

   J taking a sightseeing trip in a strange city

3 What will Jen and Nicky probably do next?

   A have lunch with Nicky's mother

   B go to the aquarium with Nicky's mother

   C go shopping with Nicky's mother

   D ride the subway to the hotel

4 Tell what happened after the train started and before it reached the next stop. Use sequence words in your answer.

_____

_____

_____

_____

5 What will Jen and Nicky probably have to do to get out of the subway?

_____

_____

_____

_____

Read the selection. Then answer the questions that follow.

Little Brown Bats

The most common bats of North America are little brown bats. Only two inches long, they are covered in fur except for their wings and feet. They have short tails and medium-sized ears. Like all bats, they can fly.

Little brown bats gather in groups called colonies. They sleep all day. Then, when the sun goes down, they fly out of their caves, trees, holes, or attics to hunt for dinner. These little creatures eat insects. A little brown bat can eat half its weight in bugs during one night.

In winter months, little brown bats hibernate. Their body temperatures lower, their breathing slows down, and they sleep until the warmer weather and insects return.

In late spring, the mother bats give birth. By the time the young bats are three weeks old, they are starting to fly and feed themselves.

Turn the page.

Answer the questions below.

1 What was the author's main purpose in this selection?

  A to add information to what scientists already know about little brown bats

  B to entertain beginning readers with a story about little brown bats

  C to express feelings about the nature of little brown bats

  D to inform the reader about brown bats

2 What was the author's main purpose in the first paragraph?

  F to describe the way the bats look

  G to give details about what the bats eat

  H to tell how the bats are useful to humans

  J to describe the social life of the bats

3 When do little brown bats do most of their eating?

  A winter, spring, and summer

  B spring, summer, and fall

  C summer, fall, and winter

  D fall, winter, and spring

4 How did the author help you picture little brown bats?

_____

_____

_____

_____

_____

_____

_____

_____

_____

_____

Read the selection. Then answer the questions that follow.

The Earth Album

Tom woke up from a nap, remembering fall in Vermont. He had just had a dream about maple trees in October, his favorite month. In his mind's eye, the trees were a dozen shades of red, yellow, and orange.

Last October, Tom's family had spent a week at a lodge in Vermont. One day they went for a walk that led them deep into the autumn woods. The trail ended at a river, where they stopped to fish. Tom's dad cooked their catch for dinner. Of course, they wouldn't be going back to Vermont for a long time.

Tom was glad he had put together a big photo album to help him remember the important events in his life. He flipped through the pages until he reached a school picture of his class from last year. Tom had a sad expression on his face, even though his parents had not yet told him of their plans. Tom wondered whether any of his friends were thinking about him right now. No, they were all probably doing ordinary things like biking, playing baseball, or even studying.

Just then, Tom's mother stepped into his cabin and said, "I have great news. Captain James says the spaceship is making excellent time. We will be landing on Planet Turnas tomorrow morning."

Turn the page.

Answer the questions below.

1 What was the author's main purpose in this story?

  A to make the reader want to travel in space

  B to entertain the reader with an unusual situation

  C to express feelings about the main character

  D to inform the reader about space travel

2 Which phrase from the third paragraph relates to its main purpose?

  F help him remember the important events

  G flipped through the pages

  H his class from last year

  J sad expression on his face

3 What would probably be the best way to read this story?

  A slowly, to hear the words in your mind

  B quietly, so as not to disturb others

  C once slowly and then again quickly

  D quickly, to find out what happened next

4 What was Tom thinking about just before his mom came into his cabin?

  F his trip to Vermont

  G maple trees in autumn

  H his friends at home

  J a walk in the woods

5 Why did the author wait to say where Tom was until the end?

_____

_____

_____

_____

_____

_____

_____

Read the selection. Then answer the questions that follow.

Carnivorous Plants

An unsuspecting fly lands on a shiny, green leaf. In less than a second, the two parts of the leaf snap together. They get tighter. It's dinnertime for this Venus's-flytrap.

The Venus's-flytrap is perhaps the best known of all carnivorous, or meat-eating, plants. There are over six hundred different species worldwide. The Venus's-flytrap and several others can be found in the southeastern part of the United States.

These amazing plants mainly eat insects, though some have been known to capture larger animals, such as small frogs. They live in swamps and other areas with poor soil. They get some food from the air and soil, as other plants do. The insects add nutrients to the plants' diet.

Carnivorous plants come in different sizes, from tiny water plants to vines many yards long. Like other plants, many meat-eaters attract insects with bright colors or sweet smells. They also have different ways of trapping their food. Some plants have sticky parts. The insect lands on them and cannot get away. Other plants have slippery parts. The insect lands, slides down into the plant, and is stuck there. Finally, some plants have suctions. When the insect comes near, it is vacuumed up. One underwater variety has the fastest trap of all. It can vacuum its prey in only 1/30 of a second.

It is good to know that these carnivores are no danger to large animals. It seems like these carnivorous plants know exactly what they want for dinner.

Turn the page.

Answer the questions below.

1 What is the author's main purpose in this selection?

   A to entertain the reader with an amazing horror story

   B to convince the reader that carnivorous plants won't hurt them

   C to explain the importance of saving carnivorous plants

   D to inform the reader about an interesting kind of plant

2 Why does the author use the phrase "carnivorous, or meat-eating, plants"?

   F to tell the reader what the word *carnivorous* means

   G to point out the difference between meat and insects

   H to make sure that the reader uses a dictionary

   J to make the plants sound dangerous

3 What is the author's purpose in the first sentence?

   A to warn the reader about a danger

   B to catch the reader's attention

   C to describe the diet of a plant

   D to show how a plant attracts insects

4 What usually happens after a carnivorous plant attracts an insect? Use sequence words in your answer.

_____

_____

_____

_____

5 What are two questions that the author answers in this selection?

_____

_____

_____

_____

Read the selection. Then answer the questions that follow.

Some Like It Hot, Some Like It Cold

When it comes to weather, the United States gets it all. Hail, rain, and snow fall in different parts of the United States. Even hurricanes and tornadoes hit parts of the country each year. Some spots, however, have bright skies on most days.

Why do some parts of the country get freezing winters while others stay warm all year? The most important reason is their distances from the equator. The equator is the imaginary line that runs around the middle of the Earth. Places closer to the equator tend to be warmer. Alaska, in the far north, is freezing cold in the winter months. By contrast, Florida, in the South, stays warm all year long. The good people of Florida are very lucky indeed.

Turn the page.

Answer the questions below.

1 What is the main idea of the first paragraph?

   A The United States gets all kinds of weather.

   B Some parts of the country get rain, hail, and snow.

   C Some places in the country have bright skies.

   D It is better to live in some states than in others.

2 Which part of the United States tends to be the warmest?

   F the North

   G the South

   H the East

   J the West

3 Which sentence from the selection is a statement of opinion?

   A Some other spots have bright skies on most days.

   B The equator is the imaginary line that runs around the middle of the Earth.

   C By contrast, Florida, in the South, stays warm all year long.

   D The good people of Florida are very lucky indeed.

4 What is the main idea of the last paragraph?

_____

_____

_____

_____

_____

_____

_____

_____

_____

Read the selection. Then answer the questions that follow.

The Big Apple

It's been called the Big Apple and America's greatest city. By any name, New York City is big. Located on the Atlantic coast, New York City covers over three hundred square miles and is home to more than eight million people. More people live in New York City than in any other city in the United States.

The Big Apple has some of the world's tallest buildings, biggest bridges, and longest tunnels. More than 150 New York City skyscrapers reach more than five hundred feet into the air. A football field is only three hundred feet long. At 4,260 feet, New York's Verrazano-Narrows Bridge is almost a mile long. That makes it the longest suspension bridge in North America and the second longest in the world. New York City also has four giant underwater tunnels.

To keep all these people happy, the Big Apple has one of the biggest city parks in the world. Central Park is 843 acres. It is an amazing place to spend time. It has its own zoo, its own castle, and its own lake. Visitors can walk, run, bike, ride horseback, roller-skate, ice-skate, and more.

In case you were wondering, all those New Yorkers also produce a large amount of garbage, about eleven thousand tons a day. Remember, you read it here.

Turn the page.

Answer the questions below.

1 What is the main idea of the selection?

  A New York City is as large as some states.

  B Some of the world's largest buildings are in New York City.

  C New York City is an interesting place to visit.

  D New York City is large in every way.

2 Which of the following details supports the main idea of paragraph two?

  F three hundred feet long

  G 4,260 feet

  H eight million people

  J five hundred feet

3 Which of these details would support the main idea of paragraph three?

  A the number of bridges built

  B the number of visitors there

  C the amount of water consumed

  D the number of trees planted

4 Which sentence from the selection is a statement of opinion?

  F It's been called the Big Apple and America's greatest city.

  G A football field is only three hundred feet long.

  H It is an amazing place to spend time.

  J Remember, you read it here.

5 What is the main idea of the fourth paragraph?

_____

_____

_____

_____

_____

_____

_____

Read the selection. Then answer the questions that follow.

National Parks

Who is the biggest landowner in the United States? The answer is our government. The landholdings of our government include huge parks, great forests, seashores, lakeshores, and rivers. About one quarter of all state land is owned by the United States government. That comes to 563 million acres.

The country's largest parks are in the largest state. Alaska has seven parks with more than a million acres each. The biggest, Wrangell–Saint Elias, has more than eight million acres. This park also has the greatest number of mountain peaks over sixteen thousand feet high.

The world's oldest national park is Yellowstone. Some would say it is also the most beautiful. In 1872 it was set aside for the people in the United States to enjoy. Yellowstone is a huge park, with more than two million acres. It has about ten thousand geysers and hot springs. The most famous geyser is known as Old Faithful. It spouts hot water just about every thirty seconds.

More people visit the Grand Canyon in Arizona than any other national park. Each year, nearly five million visitors come to look out over the canyon worn away by the Colorado River. It's a sight nobody could forget. It is nature at its best. Grand Canyon Park also has more than a million acres of land. What's more, it was one of the country's first national parks, founded in 1893. What's not to love about our country's natural treasures?

Turn the page.

Answer the questions below.

1 What is the main idea of the selection?

   A Yellowstone, founded in 1872, is the oldest national park.

   B The United States has set aside millions of acres of land for parks.

   C The most unforgettable national park is the Grand Canyon.

   D A good part of all state land is owned by the U.S. government.

2 What is the main idea of paragraph two?

   F Alaska has seven parks with more than a million acres each.

   G One park has the largest number of tall mountains.

   H Wrangell–Saint Elias has more than eight million acres.

   J The biggest state has the biggest national parks.

3 Which sentence from the selection is a statement of fact?

   A That comes to 563 million acres.

   B It is also the most beautiful.

   C It's a sight nobody could forget.

   D It is nature at its best.

4 What is the main idea of the first paragraph?

_____

_____

_____

_____

_____

5 What is the main idea of the last paragraph?

_____

_____

_____

_____

_____

Name _____

Read the selection. Then answer the questions that follow.

The Ants and the Grasshopper
Based on a fable by Aesop

There once was a grasshopper who sang and fiddled all through the summer months. His industrious neighbors, the ants, lived very differently. They worked all day and only stopped at night to rest.

"Quit your laboring. Join me in singing and dancing," the grasshopper often suggested.

"Stop your fooling around. Get ready for the winter," the ants often answered.

Soon summer gave way to winter, as it always does.

The ants nestled in their cozy holes with plenty of food. The poor grasshopper, however, was cold and starving.

"Please, let me come in and share your food," the grasshopper begged outside the ants' nest.

The ants were not sympathetic. "You fiddled and sang throughout the summer while we worked. Now you must live with the results of your decision."

Turn the page.

Answer the questions below.

1 Why did the ants have plenty of food in the winter?

    A because they lived in a cozy nest

    B because they told the grasshopper to stop fooling around

    C because they were not sympathetic to the grasshopper

    D because they worked hard all summer

2 Why didn't the ants join the grasshopper to fiddle and sing?

    F because they didn't know any songs or dances

    G because they didn't like the grasshopper

    H because they knew they needed to prepare for the winter

    J because there was plenty of food for the winter

3 Why did the grasshopper fiddle and sing all summer?

    A because the ants were doing all the work

    B because there was no work to be done

    C because there was plenty of food for the winter

    D because the gardens were full of things to eat

4 What probably happened to the grasshopper during the winter?

© Pearson Education 4

Name _____

Read the selection. Then answer the questions that follow.

Roller-skating

It was Saturday morning, the end of Jean's spring vacation. Finally the rain had stopped. "The rain stopped just in time. Now Beth and I can go roller-skating like we planned," Jean told her mother.

Beth arrived half an hour later, and the girls left under a sunny blue sky. "I was getting tired of being inside all week," Jean said.

"Me too. All the rain just about wrecked my vacation," Beth agreed.

The park was a short walk from Jean's house. They sat on a bench and laced up their skates. Then they raced along the paved path, past trees just beginning to leaf. A big family with two dogs passed them. "Hey, Jean," one of the kids shouted.

Jean turned and waved. It was her friend Patti. But as she was looking at Patti, Jean's skate hit a crack in the path. She tripped and lost her balance. She managed to fall onto the grass rather than on the hard pavement. Jean was going so fast that she slid through the wet grass and fell onto the muddy bank.

"Oh rats." When Jean stood up, her clothes were covered with mud. Beth raced over and asked, "Are you OK?"

"Yeah, I'm fine," Jean said, "but I think the rain just wrecked some more of my vacation. Why couldn't I have kept my eyes where they belonged?"

Turn the page.

Answer the questions below.

1 Why was Jean getting tired during her vacation?

  A because the rain had kept her inside all week

  B because she wanted to go to the movies

  C because she didn't want her vacation to end

  D because she missed her friends and activities at school

2 Why didn't Jean notice the crack in the sidewalk?

  F because she was looking at some dogs

  G because it was hidden under some leaves

  H because she tripped and lost her balance

  J because she turned to wave at Patti

3 Because Jean did not want to fall on the pavement, she

  A didn't notice a crack in the pavement.

  B tripped and lost her balance.

  C turned aside onto the grass.

  D turned to wave at her friend Patti.

4 What happened because Jean was skating so fast?

  F She tripped on a crack in the path.

  G She slid on the grass and fell in the mud.

  H She went skating with her friend Beth.

  J She saw a family walking a dog.

5 What did Jean blame for her accident?

_____

_____

_____

_____

_____

_____

Read the selection. Then answer the questions that follow.

The Blooper

"You're up, Mark. We need a big one," Coach Farley said.

The coach smiled, but Mark knew he was worried. It was the ninth inning and their team was behind by one run and down to their last out. To make matters worse, Mark was having a terrible day. He had struck out twice, hit three flies that were caught, and been thrown out at first base.

The first pitch flew over the plate. Mark swung and missed. The next pitch was too low and the third was too high, two balls and one strike. On the fourth pitch, Mark hit the ball hard. It went flying along the first base line and foul, two balls and two strikes.

The next pitch was low, but Mark went for it anyway. He chipped the top of the ball, and it dribbled a few yards in front of him. As Mark ran toward first base, the pitcher and catcher both raced for the ball and crashed. By the time the shortstop reached the ball, Mark was halfway to first base and their team's other runner was racing to third. The shortstop threw to first, hoping for a last out, but the first baseman missed the ball. The ball zipped past Mark. Better yet, the runner scored, and Mark was safe at first.

Now the game was tied, and Mark's team had their best hitter up at bat.

Turn the page.

Answer the questions below.

1 **Why was Coach Farley worried?**
   A Mark had swung and missed.
   B Mark was the last player of the inning.
   C The team was behind in the last inning.
   D The team had not played well up to then.

2 **Why didn't the catcher get the ball Mark chipped?**
   F Mark was already halfway to first base.
   G He ran into the pitcher.
   H The ball flew along the first base line.
   J The pitch was low.

3 **Why was Mark safe at first base?**
   A The first baseman missed the ball.
   B The shortstop threw to first.
   C His team's runner scored.
   D Mark chipped the top of the ball.

4 **Why do you think the pitcher and catcher crashed into each other?**

_____

_____

_____

_____

_____

5 **Did Mark's team have a chance of winning the game? Explain.**

_____

_____

_____

_____

Read the selection. Then answer the questions that follow.

The Swim Meet

Tina put on her bathing cap and grabbed her towel. The swim practice was about to begin. Tina got to the pool before everybody. The coach wasn't even there yet.

Coach Rice arrived a few minutes later. She smiled at Tina and said, "You've been working really hard for the meet tomorrow. I wish everybody tried so hard."

The next day, Tina was worried. She had to swim in two relay races, and she was the slowest swimmer on the relay team.

Finally, it was time for the first relay race, so Tina sat with the relay team near the pool. The first two racers did well, and now it was Tina's turn. She got in the water and pushed off. She kept telling herself that everybody was counting on her.

When Tina finished, her teammates were all cheering. "You have really improved," Coach Rice said.

Turn the page.

Answer the questions below.

1 What sentence best describes the way Tina felt about the swim meet?

   A She was sure she could help her team win.

   B She was worried but determined to do her best.

   C She knew she should not be worried about the race.

   D She wanted to make the coach proud.

2 What detail from the story supports the conclusion that Tina's team won?

   F It was time for the first relay race.

   G Tina got to the pool before everyone else.

   H Tina told herself everyone was counting on her.

   J Tina's teammates were all cheering.

3 When and where does this story take place?

   A on one day in Tina's school

   B on a Saturday at a playground

   C on two days at a swimming pool

   D during the summer at a camp

4 Do you think Tina was still the slowest swimmer on the team? Explain your answer.

_____

_____

_____

_____

_____

_____

_____

_____

_____

_____

Read the selection. Then answer the questions that follow.

The Taxi Ride

Lilly sat next to her father in the cab. He was driving a man to the airport. Lilly was on vacation today, and since her mother was working, her parents decided that Lilly would spend the day with her father—at work.

"I am flying to China today to visit my brother who's working over there," the man said.

"I've always wanted to see the Great Wall of China," Lilly's father said.

Lilly's father talked to the man all the way to the airport. Lilly found out about the man's family, his job, and other trips he had made. When the man got out, he gave Lilly's father a big tip. "Have a great trip," Lilly's father said. "And visit the Great Wall for me."

Now Lilly's father picked up another fare, a woman going into the city. "Please take me to the Park Hotel," she said. Lilly's father put her bags into the trunk.

Lilly's family lived in a small town, so she loved driving into the city. She liked seeing all the people and the tall buildings. She liked the crowded streets. She even liked the city noises.

Soon her father stopped in front of a big hotel. He carried the woman's bags up to the door, where someone else took them. Lily watched the woman thank her father and give him some dollar bills.

"Time for a break," her father said when he got back into the cab. "I know a great hotdog stand near here."

Turn the page.

Answer the questions below.

1 Why was Lilly riding with her father?

 A Her father needed her help to find his way around.

 B Her parents wanted her to learn how to drive a cab.

 C She had asked if she could ride with her father.

 D Her parents didn't want her to be home alone.

2 What best describes the way Lilly's father treated his customers?

 F He did very little to help them.

 G He was friendly and helpful.

 H He was kind and easygoing.

 J He told them a lot of jokes.

3 You can conclude that the place where Lilly lived was probably

 A quiet and uncrowded.

 B large and exciting.

 C crowded and noisy.

 D full of tall buildings.

4 This story most likely takes place

 F late at night.

 G in the evening.

 H in the morning.

 J on a weekend.

5 Do you think Lilly's father liked his job? Support your answer with a detail from the story.

_____

_____

_____

_____

_____

_____

_____

Read the selection. Then answer the questions that follow.

Maria's Saturday

"Please clean up that table for me, honey," Maria's mother said.

Some ladies were just leaving a table at Sunshine Bakery. Maria got off her stool and cleared the dishes from the empty table. She took them to the kitchen, then returned to sponge off the table.

When Maria sat down on her stool again, her mother said, "Thank you so much, honey, for being such a big help."

Maria spent most Saturdays at the family bakery. Saturdays were their busiest days, when the bakery was packed with customers. Maria's mother worked the counter with Maria's older sister. Her father baked bread and pastries all day while Maria cleared tables and brought in fresh bread from the kitchen.

The smell of fresh bread filled the bakery. Maria thought her dad's bread was the best in the world. They played jazzy music all day. No wonder people always smiled when they came into Sunshine Bakery.

Maria was shocked when her mom said that it was time to close. Maria hadn't been paying attention to the clock, and she had thought that it was much earlier in the day.

Maria locked the door, and a few minutes later, her father took out a huge pizza from the oven and set it down on one of the tables. The whole family crowded around the pizza to eat their dinner together.

Turn the page.

Answer the questions below.

1 How did Maria feel about working at the bakery on Saturdays?

   A She would have liked it more if it were less busy.

   B She liked helping her father bake bread.

   C She would rather be with her friends.

   D She enjoyed being at the bakery.

2 How did Maria probably feel at the end of the day?

   F tired but happy

   G sleepy and sad

   H bored and tired

   J angry but excited

3 The events in the story last

   A a few minutes.

   B a couple of hours.

   C from morning to evening.

   D from Saturday to Sunday.

4 Why do you think time passed so quickly for Maria?

_____

_____

_____

_____

_____

5 Why do you think the customers smiled when they came into Sunshine Bakery?

_____

_____

_____

_____

Read the selection. Then answer the questions that follow.

Vet on Wheels

Jo Barns has six cats and two dogs. She used to dread their yearly visit to the vet. Now, she just makes one phone call.

"I call Vet on Wheels," she says, "and they send out a vet who sees all my pets in one hour."

Mike Roper has just one cat, but it's a fussy Siamese. Mike hated to take her to the vet because she yowled the whole time. Now he too calls Vet on Wheels. "What a relief," he says.

Vet on Wheels is the brainchild of Liz Wells, who has been a vet in Wayford, Maine, for the last twenty years. People used to joke that she should make house calls. Then one day she took the idea seriously. "I thought, yes, I should make house calls. It makes people's lives easier, and it's good for their pets."

Turn the page.

Answer the questions below.

1 How did the Vet on Wheels customers probably feel about Liz Wells?

A angry

B fearful

C thankful

D worried

2 Why do you think Jo Barns used to dread going to the vet?

F Her animals didn't like to go.

G She had so many animals.

H The vet was so far away.

J It meant that the animals were sick.

3 What is one reason Vet on Wheels is better for pets than going to a vet?

A They eat better at home than at a vet's.

B They don't have to see a vet so often.

C They see a vet who takes care of them.

D They aren't frightened by a strange place.

4 How was Jo Barns's life different after she started calling Vet on Wheels?

_____

_____

_____

_____

_____

_____

_____

_____

_____

_____

_____

Read the selection. Then answer the questions that follow.

Fun at Winston Park

Bobbie helped her dad spread the beach blanket on the grass and set up two beach chairs. Bobbie's parents sat in the chairs. Bobbie sat on the blanket next to her little brother, Sam.

Bobbie's mom passed around paper plates, chicken, potato salad, and cups of apple juice. While Bobbie enjoyed her dinner, she noticed Winston Park fill up with blankets, beach chairs, and half the town of Winston. Some ants crossed Bobbie's blanket. She swept them off with her hand.

Bobbie's friend Mike passed by with his family. "You sure got a great spot," he said to Bobbie.

"We come here every year," Bobbie told him. "We always come early to find a good spot and have a big picnic."

"Well, I'll see you at camp tomorrow," Mike said.

When the sun started to set, an announcer asked for quiet. Then the band struck up "The Star-Spangled Banner." Everybody stood and sang along as loudly as they could. Some people could even hit the high notes. Then they settled back down and talked quietly.

At last Bobbie heard the loud booms she'd been waiting for. The sky lit up with giant sparkling flowers of red, white, and blue. Sam started to whimper and Bobbie put her arm around him. Sam leaned against her and smiled as the sky exploded into a million colors.

Turn the page.

Answer the questions below.

1 At what time of year did the story take place?

   A winter

   B spring

   C summer

   D fall

2 What word best describes how Bobbie felt about Sam?

   F proud

   G admiring

   H sad

   J protective

3 What lit up the sky at the end of the story?

   A moonlight

   B starlight

   C flashlights

   D fireworks

4 How did Sam and Bobbie feel when they first heard the booms?

   F Sam was afraid, and Bobbie was happy.

   G Sam was sad, and Bobbie was angry.

   H Sam was angry, and Bobbie was pleased.

   J They were both happy.

5 How do you know that Bobbie's family had prepared for this event?

_____

_____

_____

_____

_____

_____

_____

Read the selection. Then answer the questions that follow.

The Big-Ring Circus

Nan's Journal

Saturday, May 5, 2005

Dad took Jesse and me to the Big-Ring Circus this afternoon. The gigantic tent was packed with happy kids and parents, from the floor to the top of the tent. We were all having a great time.

Soon the overhead lights dimmed, the band started playing, and the spotlights turned on the circus parade. Riders on horses, elephants, and camels led the way. Dancers and tumblers came next, followed by the hilarious clowns.

After that, two clowns stayed in the big ring. One clown kept falling down and losing things. First he lost his hat, then his coat, and finally his shoes. The other clown kept taking things out of his hat. He filled a giant bag with the things he pulled from his hat. Then the first clown made a mess looking for his lost clothes in that huge bag. I couldn't stop laughing the whole time, and neither could anybody else.

My favorite part was watching the acrobats. They climbed ladders almost to the top of the tent. Then they started jumping from bar to bar. They swung upside down like monkeys in a jungle. They did somersaults in the air. It looked like they were flying. They also did tricks together. One acrobat would jump and another would catch her. I kept thinking somebody would fall, but they never did.

Turn the page.

Answer the questions below.

1 **Which words best describe the circus as Nan saw it?**

  A small, loud, exciting, and funny

  B big, crowded, noisy, and exciting

  C silly, loud, strange, and sad

  D quiet, funny, crowded, and dangerous

2 **Why did the lights dim and the band start playing?**

  F The show was starting.

  G The clowns were coming on stage.

  H The acrobats were about to start their act.

  J The animals were in the ring.

3 **How did Nan feel about the acrobats?**

  A They should have been more careful.

  B They were very funny.

  C Their act was exciting.

  D They were afraid of falling.

4 **How were the two clowns different?**

_____

_____

_____

_____

5 **Do you think Nan would tell her friends to go to the circus? Explain your answer.**

_____

_____

_____

_____

_____

Read the selection. Then answer the questions that follow.

Why I Love Thanksgiving

Thanksgiving is the very best day of the fall season. This national holiday falls on the fourth Thursday in November. It is a day to remember the first Americans. Banks, post offices, and most stores close for Thanksgiving Day. Schools close for the long weekend.

American families get together for a big meal. This time of being together means a lot. The centerpiece of most Thanksgiving dinners is the turkey. This all-American bird tastes great with stuffing and cranberry sauce. Sweet potatoes and other vegetables add to the feast. And don't forget pumpkin pie for dessert. Nobody leaves the table hungry on Thanksgiving.

Turn the page.

Answer the questions below.

1 **Which sentence from the first paragraph is a statement of opinion?**

    A   Thanksgiving is the very best day of the fall season.

    B   This national holiday falls on the fourth Thursday in November.

    C   Banks, post offices, and most stores close.

    D   Schools close for the long weekend.

2 **Which sentence from the second paragraph is a statement of fact?**

    F   The centerpiece of most Thanksgiving dinners is the turkey.

    G   This all-American bird tastes great with stuffing and cranberry sauce.

    H   Sweet potatoes and other vegetables add to the feast.

    J   And don't forget pumpkin pie for dessert.

3 **What is the main idea of the second paragraph?**

    A   American families love a big meal.

    B   Americans eat too much on Thanksgiving.

    C   The turkey is the most important Thanksgiving dish.

    D   American families share a big meal on Thanksgiving.

4 **Write your opinion about Thanksgiving.**

_____

_____

_____

_____

_____

_____

_____

_____

_____

_____

Read the selection. Then answer the questions that follow.

Best Job in the World

What is the best job in the world? Different people have different ideas. Some workers want to make lots of money. Other people like a job that is easy. However, many people look for a job they enjoy. Liking your work is the most important thing.

Different jobs make people happy in different ways. Many people work in the "helping professions." These are jobs that help other people. Doctors and nurses are part of this group. They work to keep people healthy. Nothing is better than helping other people to feel better.

In a way, people in show business help others too. They get us to laugh. They help us to forget our troubles. The ability to make others laugh or have fun is a great talent. Maybe that's why dozens of new movies are made every year. Watching a movie is the best way to forget what is bothering you.

Still other people enjoy making something beautiful or interesting. That is the work of artists, singers, and writers. They make paintings, songs, and books. People should spend more time looking at paintings. Nothing is nicer than listening to a good song. Then again, reading a great book comes pretty close.

In short, you do not have to worry. There is a job out there for just about every taste. That sure is lucky for all of us.

Turn the page.

Answer the questions below.

1 Which sentence from the first paragraph is a statement of opinion?

A Some workers want to make lots of money.

B Other people like a job that is easy.

C However, many people look for a job they enjoy.

D Liking your work is the most important thing.

2 Which sentence from paragraph 2 is a statement of opinion?

F Many people work in the "helping professions."

G Doctors and nurses are part of this group.

H They work to keep people healthy.

J Nothing is better than helping other people to feel better.

3 Which of these is a statement of fact?

A The ability to make others laugh or have fun is a great talent.

B Watching a movie is the best way to forget what is bothering you.

C Artists, singers, and writers make paintings, songs, and books.

D Nothing is nicer than listening to a good song.

4 What is the topic of the fourth paragraph?

F making something beautiful

G artists, singers, and writers

H looking at paintings

J reading a great book

5 What job interests you? Write a fact about that job.

_____

_____

_____

_____

_____

_____

_____

_____

© Pearson Education 4

Read the selection. Then answer the questions that follow.

Fourth-Grade Sports Survey

Mr. Frank's fourth-grade math class took a survey of students' favorite sports. First they made a list of fifteen sports. Then the students voted for their five favorite sports. The winners were swimming, soccer, baseball, basketball, and football. These five sports were used on the survey. Sailing is a great sport, but it did not make the list. Other popular sports that did not make the cut were skating, kickball, and skiing.

All fourth graders at the Lake Shore School received a survey. There are 224 fourth graders. The students had to pick only their favorite one of the five sports. It was a hard choice. All five sports are lots of fun and exciting.

The survey found that baseball was the favorite sport of most students. In all, 63 of the 224 students picked baseball. The number-two spot went to soccer, with 57 students. Basketball was a close third, with 50 students. Swimming and football each received 27 votes.

The survey results seem strange to me. To my mind, swimming is much more fun than basketball or football. Swimming is also the best way to get exercise. People can swim year-round in an indoor pool. Basketball is the only other sport in the group that can be played year-round in places with cold winters.

What is your favorite sport?

Turn the page.

Answer the questions below.

1 Which sentence from the first paragraph is a statement of opinion?

   A First they made a list of fifteen sports.

   B Then the students voted for their five favorite sports.

   C These five sports were used on the survey.

   D Sailing is a great sport, but it did not make the list.

2 Which sentence from paragraph 2 is a statement of opinion?

   F All fourth graders at the Lake Shore School received a survey.

   G There are 224 fourth graders.

   H The students had to pick only their favorite one of the five sports.

   J All five sports are lots of fun and exciting.

3 Which sentence from the last two paragraphs is a statement of fact?

   A The survey results seem strange to me.

   B To my mind, swimming is much more fun than basketball or football.

   C Swimming is also the best way to get exercise.

   D People can swim year-round in an indoor pool.

4 What is your favorite sport? Write an opinion about it.

_____

_____

_____

_____

_____

5 What is the main idea of paragraph 3?

_____

_____

_____

_____

_____

Read the selection. Then answer the questions that follow.

Baseball Hall of Fame

Every year, more than 350,000 people visit the National Baseball Hall of Fame and Museum in Cooperstown, New York. The museum houses more than 130,000 baseball cards and 35,000 objects. Bats, balls, and gloves from many of baseball's best players are there. For many people, the Hall of Fame brings baseball history to life.

Why Cooperstown? In 1905, a group of baseball bigwigs wanted to discover when baseball began. They carried out a three-year study. Many people shared their ideas about the beginnings of baseball. The group found that the first baseball game was in Cooperstown, New York, in 1839.

Later, they decided to celebrate the first hundred years of baseball in Cooperstown. Plans were also made to honor baseball's top players. The first Hall of Famers were picked in 1936. The National Baseball Hall of Fame and Museum opened on June 12, 1939. The crowds have been coming to Cooperstown ever since.

Turn the page.

Answer the questions below.

1 What is the main idea of the first paragraph?

A The Baseball Hall of Fame attracts crowds to view its large collection.

B The National Baseball Hall of Fame and Museum is in Cooperstown.

C There are more than 35,000 objects in the Hall of Fame museum.

D The Hall of Fame brings baseball history to life.

2 What is the main idea of paragraph 2?

F A group of baseball bigwigs got together.

G These important people carried out a three-year study.

H Many people shared their ideas about when baseball had started.

J Baseball began in Cooperstown in 1839.

3 Which sentence from the selection is a generalization?

A For many people, the Hall of Fame brings baseball history to life.

B The first baseball game was in Cooperstown, New York.

C Plans were also made to honor baseball's top players.

D The National Hall of Fame and Museum opened on June 12, 1939.

4 What is the topic of this selection?

_____

_____

_____

_____

_____

_____

_____

_____

_____

_____

_____

Read the selection. Then answer the questions that follow.

Work Dogs

Does your dog sleep the day away? Is its only job to look cute? Does it only wake up to eat dinner or play ball? Believe it or not, some dogs are not just pets. Some dogs work for their living.

Many blind people count on dogs with special training. These guide dogs go wherever their owners go. They help their owners move safely from place to place. They learn to stop at busy streets. They help their owners stay out of danger.

Search dogs find people who get lost or trapped. Dogs have a much stronger sense of smell than people. They use their noses to track down hikers lost in the woods. They find people trapped in buildings after an earthquake. They help save lives.

Many dogs protect people and property. Some dogs are trained to watch farm animals. For example, they may keep sheep from getting lost. Other dogs guard homes and shops. Still others work for the police, helping to find people who have done crimes.

Dogs also have jobs in show business. You can see them on TV, in movies, in plays, and in circuses. These dogs have to be smart and well trained. Circus dogs learn to do amazing tricks. Dogs also show up in TV ads.

Whatever they do, though, whether as workers or pets, dogs are the greatest!

Turn the page.

Answer the questions below.

1 **What is the topic of this selection?**

   A blind people

   B working dogs

   C guard dogs

   D dog owners

2 **What is the main idea of paragraph 2?**

   F Guide dogs get special training.

   G Guide dogs learn to stop at busy streets.

   H Guide dogs are good for blind people.

   J Guide dogs help keep blind people safe.

3 **What is the main idea of paragraph 3?**

   A Dogs have a stronger sense of smell than people do.

   B Search dogs find people who get lost or trapped.

   C Dogs can track down lost hikers by following their noses.

   D Dogs can sometimes save lives.

4 **Which sentence from the selection is not a generalization?**

   F Does your dog sleep the day away?

   G Many blind people count on dogs with special training.

   H Other dogs guard homes and shops.

   J These dogs have to be smart and well trained.

5 **What is the main idea of the selection?**

_____

_____

_____

_____

_____

_____

_____

Read the selection. Then answer the questions that follow.

On Top of the News

Do you like learning new things? Do you enjoy meeting new people and finding out about their lives? Do you like to discover surprising facts? Do you think that writing is fun? If you answered yes to these questions, you might make a great newspaper reporter.

A reporter writes stories for newspapers. Most reporters cover a "beat," such as sports, crime, or local news. Local news stories tell readers what is happening in their town. A flood, a train accident, or a new movie could be the subject of a story. Other stories cover news in other parts of the state, country, or world.

How does a reporter get the facts for a news story? By talking to many people, on the phone or in person, and by doing research in the library or on the Internet. Reporting a story takes time and hard work.

Reporters must find out whether their sources are reliable. They have to be careful and double-check their work. They have to make sure that their facts are correct.

Finally, a reporter has to write the story. The opening, or lead, must be catchy to get the reader's attention. The body of the story must answer questions about the topic. A good news story ends with a kicker. This is a final statement that sums things up in an interesting way.

Turn the page.

Answer the questions below.

1 What is the topic of this selection?

   A writing a news story

   B what newspaper reporters do

   C what to be when you grow up

   D doing research

2 What is the main idea of paragraph 3?

   F How does a reporter get the facts for a news story?

   G Reporters do research in the library and on the Internet to get facts.

   H Reporters talk to people and do research to get facts for a story.

   J Reporting a story takes time and hard work.

3 Which sentence is a generalization?

   A Do you think that writing is fun?

   B Most reporters cover a "beat," such as sports.

   C The body of a story must answer questions.

   D Finally, a reporter has to write the story.

4 What is the main idea of the selection?

_____

_____

_____

_____

_____

5 What is a detail that supports the main idea of the last paragraph?

_____

_____

_____

_____

_____

Read the selection. Then answer the questions that follow.

Cleaning the Purple Martin House

When the days grew warm, most birds flew north to cooler places. The birdhouses stood empty, and Chan Sook's father decided it was time to clean them.

Mostly, Chan Sook enjoyed this job. She liked the warm sun on her shoulders, and she liked talking with her father. She liked working hard and then knowing the work was finished.

She didn't like cleaning the big purple martin house, though. It had dozens of little holes, and every year, a snake came out of one of them.

Chan Sook stood back while her father lowered the purple martin house. As usual, a long, black snake slithered out, and they watched it disappear into the tall grass.

Turn the page.

Answer the questions below.

1 Why were there no birds in the birdhouses?

   A The snake ate them.

   B Chan Sook and her father scared them away.

   C They flew north for the summer.

   D They were hiding in the tall grass.

2 Why didn't Chan Sook like cleaning the purple martin house?

   F It was dirtier than the others.

   G She was afraid of snakes.

   H It was too tall for her to reach.

   J Its holes were hard to clean.

3 What was one reason Chan Sook liked cleaning the other birdhouses?

   A Her father paid her for helping.

   B She liked seeing the birds.

   C Her father made a game of it.

   D She liked working outside.

4 Describe a job that you sometimes do. Explain how it is like or different from cleaning birdhouses.

_____

_____

_____

_____

_____

_____

_____

_____

_____

Read the selection. Then answer the questions that follow.

Sandra's Ribbon

Sandra Soto entered a storytelling contest. To prepare, she told her story to her parents. She began with her name, even though they already knew her name. She used her face and her hands to help tell the story. She looked straight into her parents' eyes as she talked. The judges would be watching for all these things.

The day of the contest, Sandra felt nervous. The judges were strangers. Everyone was watching her. Her parents were not even there. Her voice shook as she began. She used her face, her hands, and her words to tell the story, just as she had done at home. The judges smiled when she looked at them, and Sandra's fear fell away. Then, as she sat down, she remembered something. She had not told the judges her name.

It was hard to listen to the other stories after that. All Sandra could think about was her own mistake. When everyone had finished, she whispered to her teacher, "May I go to the library?"

"Don't you want to know if you won a ribbon?" asked the teacher.

Sandra shook her head. She knew there would be no ribbon. As she stood up to leave, one of the judges asked her name.

"Sandra Soto," she said.

The judge said, "Our third-place ribbon goes to Sandra Soto for her story, 'The Robin and the Worm.'"

Turn the page.

Answer the questions below.

1 Why did Sandra tell her parents her name?

   A She needed to remind herself.

   B She was practicing for the contest.

   C She had a different name for the contest.

   D She wanted to remind them of her story.

2 What happened when Sandra became nervous at the contest?

   F She did everything perfectly.

   G She couldn't remember the story.

   H She forgot to give her name.

   J She didn't look at the judges.

3 Why did the judges smile at Sandra?

   A They knew her parents.

   B They had heard her story before.

   C Her story was funny.

   D She told her story well.

4 Why did Sandra want to leave?

   F She felt she'd done poorly.

   G Everyone else was leaving.

   H She wanted to find a different story.

   J Her parents were waiting for her.

5 How was the contest different from practicing at home? Write one difference below.

_____

_____

_____

_____

_____

_____

_____

_____

Read the selection. Then answer the questions that follow.

A Sea Turtle Named Alice

Eric and his mother went to the aquarium. They walked into a huge room. In front of them stood a great glass tank filled with water and rocks. A wide ramp wrapped around the outside of the tank.

They started up the ramp. From there, they saw many creatures swimming among the rocks inside the tank. Eric put his face against the glass. He spotted a clam hiding in the sand. A nurse shark swam past without looking at him. Then a giant sea turtle glided by. It slowly flapped its flippers as it swam. "It looks like it's flying," said Eric.

An aquarium worker walked up beside him. She said, "That's Alice. Someone found her on the beach and called us. A boat had bumped into her. She was so badly injured that she couldn't swim. As you can see, she's doing better now. We'll set her free next month."

Eric said, "So this place is like a hospital. Was the shark hurt too? Is that why it's here?"

"No," said the worker. "Some animals are here to help us learn. There are many things we don't know about the ocean and the creatures that live there. That shark has a lot to teach us."

"Can't you learn from Alice too?" asked Eric's mother.

The worker smiled. "Alice is too big to stay in our tank. She needs more room to swim."

Turn the page.

Answer the questions below.

1 In the second paragraph, Eric compares the sea turtle to

  A a fish.

  B a shark.

  C a bird.

  D a clam.

2 Why couldn't Alice swim when she first arrived at the aquarium?

  F The tank was too small.

  G She had been hit by a boat.

  H She did not know how.

  J She was afraid of the shark.

3 What was the main reason that Alice was kept in the aquarium?

  A so scientists could study her

  B so she could take care of the younger turtles

  C so people would pay money to see her

  D so she could get well

4 What sentence tells you why Alice could not stay in the aquarium?

_____

_____

_____

_____

5 Why do you think people visit aquariums? Explain by giving an example from the selection.

_____

_____

_____

_____

_____

_____

Read the selection. Then answer the questions that follow.

Tree of Life

Imagine a tree that is a thousand years old. Some baobab trees may be more ancient than that! The trunks of older trees are so large that people use them for shops, hiding places, and barns.

I believe no other plant is as useful as this one. People boil its leaves and then eat them, like spinach. They make a drink packed with vitamins from the fruit of the baobab tree. Its slick, pink bark is used to make baskets, rope, and cloth.

People tell stories about this wonderful tree. They call it the Tree of Life, and the name fits, I think. Birds, bats, baboons, and squirrels live in it. For that matter, even people have built houses inside baobab trees.

Turn the page.

Answer the questions below.

1 Which of these is a statement of the author's opinion about baobab trees?

   A People cook its leaves and then eat them.

   B They make a drink from its fruit.

   C The name fits, I think.

   D Birds, bats, and monkeys live in it.

2 What generalization can readers make after reading this selection?

   F Every baobab tree has animals living in it.

   G People use many parts of the baobab tree.

   H There are no small baobab trees.

   J Baobab trees are always beautiful.

3 What clue words tell you that the following sentence is a statement of opinion?

   "I believe no plant is more useful than this one."

   A I believe

   B no plant

   C more useful

   D this one

4 The following sentence states both a fact and an opinion. What is the statement of fact in this sentence? What is the statement of opinion?

   "People tell stories about this wonderful tree."

_____

_____

_____

_____

_____

_____

_____

_____

Read the selection. Then answer the questions that follow.

Book Sale Starts Today

Have you read any good books lately? If you're looking for something to read, you'll want to visit the Adams School Library, where the exciting Fall Book Sale starts today and runs all week. Every year, students collect books from people in the neighborhood and sell them to raise money for a good cause. This gives you good prices on great books.

When you walk in the door, someone will give you a large bag. Fill the bag with books, and pay only five dollars for the whole bag. These are the same books your friends have been reading, so you know they are good.

There will be a special sale of new books on Tuesday. These books have been given to the school by bookstores. The prices on these are a bit higher, but still not as high as you would find in a store. You will not find a better deal anywhere.

Money from this year's sale will help pay for a sidewalk from the school to the playground. This is important because, now, students have to walk through mud every time they go out to recess.

If you or someone you know likes to read, come and check out this sale. The Adams School Library opens at 8:00 A.M. and closes at 4:00 P.M. Be sure to call if you have any questions, but don't miss it!

Turn the page.

Answer the questions below.

1 What sentence from the selection states both a fact and an opinion?

  A Have you read any good books lately?

  B The exciting Fall Book Sale starts today and runs all week.

  C Every year, students collect books from people in the neighborhood.

  D These are the same books your friends have been reading.

2 Which of these is a statement of fact?

  F You'll want to visit the Adams School Library.

  G You know they are good.

  H Come and check out this sale.

  J The Adams School Library opens at 8:00 A.M.

3 What clue word helps you know that the following statement is a generalization?

  "You will not find a better deal anywhere."

  A not

  B better

  C deal

  D anywhere

4 What clue words help you know that the following sentence states an opinion?

  "This gives you good prices on great books."

  F *This* and *prices*

  G *good* and *great*

  H *gives* and *good*

  J *on* and *books*

5 Explain how the following statement of fact could be proved true or false.

  "Now, students have to walk through mud every time they go out to recess."

_____

_____

_____

_____

_____

_____

Read the selection. Then answer the questions that follow.

A Letter to a Friend

Dear Susan,

I just finished reading a great book, and I know you're going to like it too. That's why I'm sending it to you. It's called *Secrets of Long Shadow Swamp,* and as you might have guessed, it's a mystery. In the story, the Carter family moves into a house beside a swamp. Then the main character, Emma Carter, sees people slipping into the swamp at night. When she tells her parents, they think she's imagining the whole thing. Emma knows something is not right, and she wants to find out what is going on at the swamp.

I know you will like this book because you liked *The Mystery of Moon Lake* and *Mysterious James January.* This one is even better! The characters are interesting, and they act like real people. It's a little scary in some parts, like when Emma and her father enter the swamp. That part gave me goose bumps. The book is 371 pages long and full of excitement. I like a book that keeps me turning the pages fast, and this book is definitely a page-turner.

The author is Carlos Flores. Have you heard of him? He has written several other mysteries. I've read two of them. In fact, the last five books I've read have been mysteries.

Give it to someone else when you finish reading it. Write back to me soon—I miss you.

Your friend,

Daniel

Turn the page.

Answer the questions below.

1 What statement from the selection states an opinion?

    A It's called *Secrets of Long Shadow Swamp*.

    B This one is even better!

    C He has written several other mysteries.

    D I've read two of them.

2 What statement from the letter states a fact?

    F I just finished reading a great book.

    G I know you're going to like it too.

    H The author is Carlos Flores.

    J It's a little scary in some parts.

3 What generalization can be made after reading this letter?

    A Susan does not enjoy reading.

    B Susan and Daniel read only mystery stories.

    C Daniel reads more books than Susan.

    D Many of the books Daniel reads are mysteries.

4 Tell the fact and the opinion in the following statement:

    "The book is 371 pages long and full of excitement."

_____

_____

_____

_____

5 Write two sentences about a book you have read. In one sentence state an opinion, and in the other sentence state a fact.

_____

_____

_____

_____

Read the selection. Then answer the questions that follow.

Owls

Owls live in most countries of the world. They are meat-eaters and hunt insects or small animals. The feathers on an owl's wings are soft and loose. This helps the owl fly without sound and makes it a good hunter. A few owls hunt during the day, but most are creatures of the night. They have sharp hearing, so they can find their prey in the dark.

The littlest owl is about the size of your hand, from wrist to fingertip. It is the elf owl. It lives in deserts of the Southwestern United States. Most owls are bigger, though. One of the largest is the great gray owl. Standing beside you, it would reach your waist or even higher.

Turn the page.

Answer the questions below.

1 What clue word tells you that the following sentence is a generalization?

"Owls live in most countries of the world."

A live

B most

C countries

D world

2 What helps owls fly quietly?

F their soft, loose wing feathers

G their sharp sense of hearing

H their habit of flying at night

J their size and the things they eat

3 What generalization can readers make from this selection?

A All owls hunt at night.

B Most owls live in deserts.

C Owls are different sizes.

D Few owls are hunters.

4 What generalization can you make about elf owls?

_____

_____

_____

_____

_____

_____

_____

_____

_____

_____

Read the selection. Then answer the questions that follow.

Potters, Diggers, Hornets, and Yellow Jackets

What's that round, gray clump stuck to the wall outside your window? It looks like a round ball of dried mud, but it's *buzzing!* Wait—something is crawling out of it. It's a wasp, and that clump is its nest.

There are about twenty-five thousand different types of wasps. Most experts divide them into two groups: social and solitary wasps. Social wasps build nests out of chewed wood, like the one described above. Inside the nest, there are tiny pockets for wasps and their eggs. Hundreds of insects may live in one nest, and the nest may be several inches across. Hornets, yellow jackets, and paper wasps are all social wasps.

Solitary wasps like to do things their own way. They don't share their nests with hundreds of other wasps. They build smaller nests for their own families. Some, like the diggers, make homes in the ground or in rotting wood. Potter wasps use mud to build tiny "pots" on bushes or trees.

All wasps are alike in certain ways. Adults have a body that is divided into two parts, with a narrow part in the middle. They have six legs, and mouths that can chew or drink.

Most have stingers that are used to protect themselves and their eggs. A wasp sting hurts because it contains a small amount of poison. Most wasps also have four wings, and many are beautiful, with stripes and bright colors.

Turn the page.

Answer the questions below.

1 How many legs do all wasps have?

  A two

  B four

  C six

  D eight

2 Which statement from the selection is a generalization?

  F "It's a wasp, and that clump is its nest."

  G "There are about twenty-five thousand different types of wasps."

  H "Inside the nest, there are tiny pockets for wasps and their eggs."

  J "Most have stingers that are used to protect themselves and their eggs."

3 What makes a wasp's sting hurt?

  A Wasps have sharp teeth.

  B The stinger has poison in it.

  C Most people are allergic to wasps.

  D A wasp's stinger goes deep into the skin.

4 What generalization can readers make about solitary wasps?

  F Solitary wasps live in small groups.

  G Solitary wasps build nests from mud.

  H Solitary wasps sting each other.

  J Solitary wasps eat wood.

5 Write three generalizations about the bodies of wasps.

_____

_____

_____

_____

_____

_____

_____

Read the selection. Then answer the questions that follow.

What Is a Glacier?

In the world's coldest places, snow almost never melts. Year after year, it piles up. Pressing down on itself, the snow turns into ice. Then the heavy ice begins to slide downhill. This moving ice, this "river of ice," is called a *glacier*.

You cannot see a glacier move. It is much too slow. The fastest ones move less than the length of a football field in a day. Most move much more slowly.

You might think you would find glaciers only at the north and south poles, but that is not true. Every continent except Australia has glaciers.

Some form high in the mountains, where it is cold all year long. The ice in these glaciers slides down the mountain very slowly. When it reaches warmer air, it melts. While ice is melting near the bottom, more snow falls at the top. More snow turns into ice, while always sliding down. In this way, the glacier flows like a river.

Some glaciers are great sheets of ice that cover the land. The ice sheet in Antarctica is the world's largest. It covers millions of square miles. While it moves very slowly, smaller glaciers flow inside it. The smaller ones move faster, flowing to the ocean. There, they drop great blocks of ice into the sea. These blocks of ice are icebergs, like the one that sank the *Titanic*.

Turn the page.

Answer the questions below.

1 Which of these sentences is a generalization?

   A Some glaciers are very large.

   B Antarctica has the largest ice sheet.

   C One ice sheet covers millions of square miles.

   D The *Titanic* hit an iceberg.

2 What causes glaciers to move?

   F earthquakes

   G gravity

   H loud noises

   J smaller glaciers

3 Which of these is a valid generalization?

   A Snow never melts in the mountains.

   B All glaciers are at the north pole.

   C Glaciers form in very cold places.

   D Glaciers never move.

4 What valid generalization can you make about icebergs?

_____

_____

_____

_____

5 What is the first generalization in this selection?

_____

_____

_____

_____

_____

Read the selection. Then answer the questions that follow.

Rosa Lopez Reads Again!

Rosa's teacher often told her class, "Reading builds a good mind." Books filled her room so that students would have plenty to read. She kept charts on her desk like the one you see below. There was a chart for each student. When students wanted to borrow a book, they would keep a record on their chart.

Rosa Lopez came up to her teacher's desk with a book in her hand. She made a note on her chart and gave it to her teacher. Her teacher read it and asked, "Do you know how to ride horses, Rosa?"

"Yes," Rosa said. "My aunt lives on a ranch, and she showed me how to ride the horses there."

?

Date Borrowed	Date Returned	Title	Author	Comments
August 30	September 9	A Horse Named Storm	Lee Carson	Great story!
September 9	September 28	Maggie's Wild Horse	G. West	Sad ending
October 6		Horse Families	Anna Rubio	

Turn the page.

Answer the questions below.

1 **Why did Rosa's teacher ask her if she knew how to ride horses?**

   A Her teacher gave horseback riding lessons.

   B Her teacher wanted Rosa to learn to ride.

   C Rosa often talked about riding horses.

   D All the books Rosa borrowed were about horses.

2 **How did Rosa feel about the book *A Horse Named Storm*?**

   F She felt the ending was too sad.

   G She enjoyed reading it.

   H She didn't finish it.

   J She thought it was boring.

3 **Which of these would be the best title for the chart?**

   A Horses Around the World

   B Rosa's Favorite Books

   C Books Borrowed by Rosa Lopez

   D Comments about Books and Authors

4 **What does the chart tell you about Rosa?**

_____

_____

_____

_____

_____

_____

_____

_____

_____

Read the selection. Then answer the questions that follow.

The Shy Octopus

Crawling fast across the ocean floor, an octopus looks for a hiding place. It finds a crab in the sand and eats it. Then the octopus settles into a small hole among some rocks. Its skin changes color to match the rocks, helping it hide. Feeling safe, the octopus looks around for food.

A minute later, an eel frightens the shy octopus. The octopus shoots a cloud of dark liquid into the water. Under cover of its "ink cloud," the octopus hurries away.

The octopus has two large eyes. It can see very well. This helps it hunt for food and look out for its enemies. It has a soft body with a head, a trunk, and a "skirt." Eight arms are connected to the skirt. There are two rows of suckers on each arm. In the center of the skirt is a mouth like a beak.

The octopus can move in two different ways. It can use its long arms to pull itself along, or it can use its siphon. The siphon is a sort of tube. The octopus pushes water out of the tube, and as the water shoots out one way, the octopus shoots off in the other.

The octopus lives in warm, salty water in most places around the world. Some octopuses are small, only a few inches in length. Others grow to be as long as a car.

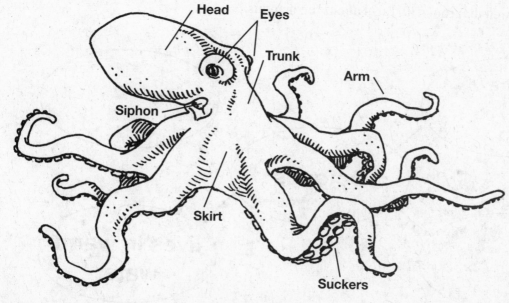

Turn the page.

Answer the questions below.

1 Why does the octopus shoot out an ink cloud?

   A to catch its food

   B to warn its friends

   C to kill its enemies

   D to hide itself

2 Where is the octopus's eye?

   F in the center of the skirt

   G near the bottom of the trunk

   H above the siphon

   J at the end of an arm

3 What is the longest part of the octopus?

   A the skirt and arms

   B the head and eye

   C the trunk

   D the siphon

4 What is the best title for the picture?

   F Parts of the Octopus

   G How an Octopus Moves

   H Where the Octopus Lives

   J Enemies of the Octopus

5 Complete the web diagram with facts about the octopus.

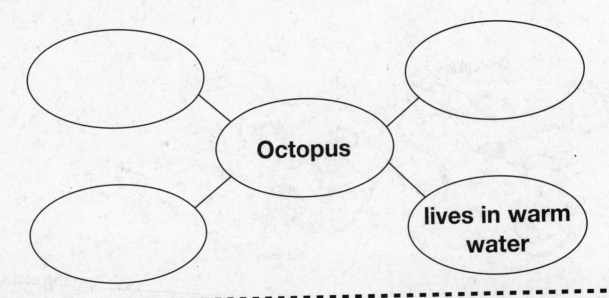

© Pearson Education 4

Read the selection. Then answer the questions that follow.

Caitlin's Science Fair Project

Science was Caitlin's favorite subject, so naturally she was excited about the Science Fair. For her project, Caitlin wanted to find out if noise and other distractions made it harder to do homework.

To find out, she read from her social studies book while other things were going on around her. She read in the same room where her brother was watching a television program. She read while listening to her favorite music group. She read in a quiet room. Then she read in a room crowded with family members talking to one another. She also read on the school bus on her way to school.

She read from the same book each time, but she didn't read the same pages she had read before. She read for the same length of time in each situation. Then she recorded the number of pages she was able to read. Finally, Caitlin made this poster to take to the Science Fair.

Do Distractions Make It Hard to Do Homework?

What Was Happening	Pages Read	Number of Minutes	Reading Speed
Television on	2	30	4 pages per hour
Jet Girls on stereo	8	30	16 pages per hour
Quiet room	7	30	14 pages per hour
Noisy room	5	30	11 pages per hour
On school bus	4	30	12 pages per hour

Conclusion Some kinds of distractions do make it hard to think.

Turn the page.

© Pearson Education 4

Answer the questions below.

1 How fast did Caitlin read while listening to music?

    A 4 pages per hour

    B 11 pages per hour

    C 14 pages per hour

    D 16 pages per hour

2 What was happening in the room Caitlin called "Noisy room"?

    F The television was playing.

    G Music was playing.

    H People were talking.

    J Machines were running.

3 What was happening when Caitlin read the fewest pages?

    A The television was playing.

    B Family members were talking.

    C The stereo was playing.

    D She was on the school bus.

4 Why did Caitlin read her social studies book instead of one of her favorite stories or a magazine?

_____

_____

_____

_____

5 Where was the best place for Caitlin to do her homework? Use information from the poster to explain your answer.

_____

_____

_____

_____

Read the selection. Then answer the questions that follow.

The Slow Sloth

In a forest of Central or South America, a sloth hangs in the trees. It hooks its huge, curved claws over a tree branch, where it hangs upside down for several days at a time. The long legs of the sloth need to be strong to support its weight. Tiny plants called algae grow in its hair, giving the animal a greenish color. This helps the sloth hide from its enemies.

The sloth's name means "laziness." It moves slowly whenever it moves at all.

The sloth rarely climbs down from the trees. Since it eats mainly leaves and small branches, food is all around. On the ground, its huge claws make walking difficult. So it "hangs out" in the trees most of the time, eating and sleeping.

Turn the page.

Answer the questions below.

1 Which statement from the selection is a generalization about sloths?

  A It hooks its huge, curved claws over a tree branch.

  B Tiny plants called algae grow in its hair.

  C The sloth's name means "laziness."

  D So it "hangs out" in the trees most of the time.

2 The author probably wrote this selection to

  F encourage readers to visit South America.

  G give information about the sloth.

  H explain how to find a sloth.

  J describe the beauty of Central American forests.

3 Which of the following is a valid generalization?

  A Sloths are well suited for life in trees.

  B Sloths are always lazy.

  C Sloths are impossible to find.

  D Sloths never leave the trees.

4 Write two generalizations that can be made about the sloth to justify its name.

_____

_____

_____

_____

_____

_____

_____

_____

_____

_____

_____

Read the selection. Then answer the questions that follow.

Cities in the Sea

Coral reefs are like great cities in the sea. Millions of creatures live in them. They always lie in warm, clear ocean water. This is because the corals that build them need warmth and sunlight to live.

These creatures are cousins of the jellyfish. They eat tiny plants and animals that float in the water. They are shaped like short tubes, and grow one on top of another. They pile up, like apartment buildings for fish. Over time, some die and others grow on their bones. Fish and other sea creatures add to the pile. Sand fills the spaces between them. In this way, over many years, reefs are made. Some are thousands of years old and cover many miles.

Fish, sea snakes, and other sea animals move in. In fact, the area becomes crowded with life, just like a city. These city dwellers find holes that offer safety from their enemies. They eat the tiny plants and animals that drift in the water. Many more eat each other.

People eat the animals that live there too. We also make medicines from some of them. Many people take vacations near reefs so they can dive around them. They enjoy seeing the beautiful creatures that live and hunt there. However, we must take care of these cities in the sea. Pollution, boating, fishing, and change in climate can all harm the corals.

Turn the page.

Answer the questions below.

1 What clue word tells you that the following sentence is a generalization?

"Pollution, boating, fishing, and change in climate can all harm the corals."

A and

B change

C can

D all

2 What sentence from the selection is not a generalization?

F They always lie in warm, clear ocean water.

G Sand fills the spaces between them.

H Some are thousands of years old.

J Many people take vacations near reefs.

3 Why might the author have written this selection?

A to inform readers about coral reefs

B to entertain readers with a sad tale

C to express excitement about diving

D to persuade readers not to eat fish

4 What valid generalization can readers make about coral reefs?

F Coral reefs are found in all warm, clear water.

G People find many uses for coral reefs.

H Most of the world's fish live in coral reefs.

J Few coral reefs are left in the world.

5 What generalizations does the author make about cities?

_____

_____

_____

_____

_____

_____

_____

Read the selection. Then answer the questions that follow.

Arctic Tundra

What Is It?

Tundra is mostly flat land in areas that are too cold for trees to grow. Most of the world's tundra is inside the Arctic Circle. In these areas, soil beneath the top layer stays frozen all the time. This frozen soil is called permafrost.

Temperatures stay below freezing for most of the year. Summers are always short, and very little rain or snow falls. Water that does fall does not drain away, because the land is flat and mostly frozen. This means that when the weather warms up in the summer, much of the land turns into a muddy swamp.

Wildlife

Mosquitoes love swamps, and in the summer months the air is thick with them. Some birds nest in the bushes in summer and then fly south when the long winter sets in. Reindeer and other grazing animals eat low-growing plants. A few kinds of hares and rabbits do too. In turn, foxes, wolves, snowy owls, and bears eat these animals. Compared with other places, the tundra is home to very few plants and animals. The climate is just too hard.

People

It doesn't sound like a great place to live, does it? The truth is, the arctic tundra is beautiful in its way. Some people do choose to live there. For a few groups in the United States and in Russia, this cold, lonely, and beautiful place is home.

Turn the page.

Answer the questions below.

1 What clue word tells you that the following sentence is a generalization?

"Most of the world's tundra is inside the Arctic Circle."

   A most

   B world's

   C is

   D inside

2 Which of these sentences from the selection is not a generalization?

   F This frozen soil is called permafrost.

   G Summers are always short.

   H Mosquitoes love swamps.

   J The arctic tundra is beautiful in its way.

3 Which of these is a valid generalization about the arctic tundra?

   A Most animals that live there are meat-eaters.

   B Winters are always long and cold.

   C It never snows there.

   D Snowy owls find plenty of food there.

4 Give two generalizations from the selection that support the following statement.

The arctic tundra doesn't sound like a great place to live.

_____

_____

_____

_____

5 Why do you think the author included section headings?

_____

_____

_____

_____

Read the selection. Then answer the questions that follow.

Gathering Leaves

Alyssa's class was collecting autumn leaves for the bulletin board. When Alyssa went to the park to gather some, she met a boy from her class. "Hey, Lucas," said Alyssa.

"Hey," said Lucas, as he dropped a flawless, star-shaped leaf into a paper sack.

"That's a nice one," said Alyssa. She scooped up an armful of leaves from a pile beside the path and stuffed them into her sack.

"It's from a sycamore tree," answered Lucas. He inspected a red, heart-shaped leaf for a moment before discarding it.

Alyssa stared. The leaf was as intensely red as a valentine, so bright she couldn't stop looking at it. The sycamore leaves were fine, but this tiny red one was a treasure. She picked it up and dropped it into her sack.

As Lucas chose a second perfect sycamore leaf, Alyssa kicked noisily through a drift and scooped another armful.

Turn the page.

Answer the questions below.

1 To what did the author compare the small red leaf?

   A   a star

   B   a person

   C   a fish

   D   a valentine

2 What word best describes Lucas?

   F   shy

   G   helpless

   H   careful

   J   loud

3 How was Alyssa's method of gathering leaves different from Lucas's?

   A   Alyssa took her time.

   B   Alyssa picked up only red ones.

   C   Alyssa gathered them by the armful.

   D   Alyssa knew the names of the trees.

4 Describe one way that Lucas and Alyssa were different and one way that they were alike.

_____

_____

_____

_____

_____

_____

_____

_____

_____

_____

Read the selection. Then answer the questions that follow.

The Poster

"The book says it's a white-crowned wren," said Andrew. "You can tell because the white stripes on its head look like a crown."

"Hello, Your Majesty," Habib joked as he sketched in the stripes on the bird he was drawing. As he drew, he glanced back and forth from the bird to his sketchbook. When the drawing was done, he ripped out the page and handed it to Andrew, who made a note on a card: "White-crowned wren, seen April 9 in Habib's yard."

"That's it," said Andrew with satisfaction. "That's the last one."

They took the drawing inside, and Habib glued it to the last empty spot on their poster. The science project was finished. They had found twenty-eight kinds of birds and looked each one up in Andrew's book *Birds of North America*. Andrew had written a note card for each bird, and Habib had put together the poster.

The poster had a drawing or photograph for every bird. Andrew liked taking photographs because they showed exactly what the bird looked like. Habib liked drawing. It took longer but made him feel that he knew more about the bird, after looking at it for so long. So half the birds were pictured in photos and the other half in drawings.

Tomorrow in school they would present their poster to the class and use the note cards to tell about the birds. Habib could hardly wait!

Turn the page.

Answer the questions below.

1 In the second paragraph, to what did Habib compare the white-crowned wren?

   A a tiger's stripes

   B a painting

   C a king or queen

   D another bird

2 What is one way Habib's pictures were different from Andrew's?

   F They looked more like birds.

   G They took longer to make.

   H They were more colorful.

   J They were smaller.

3 What is probably one reason that Andrew and Habib were friends?

   A They had the same skills and talents.

   B Both liked to make jokes and kid around.

   C They grew up next door to each other.

   D They were interested in the same things.

4 What answer best completes the chart?

How the Work Was Shared

Habib	Andrew
made 14 drawings	took 14 photos
made the poster	?

   F wrote the note cards

   G owned *Birds of North America*

   H liked photographs

   J took the drawing inside

5 Do you think the work was divided fairly? Use details from the selection to explain your answer.

_____

_____

_____

_____

Read the selection. Then answer the questions that follow.

A Change of Heart

Richard gazed out the classroom windows and didn't like what he saw. The trees along the playing field were covered in white blossoms, as they had been all week. For Richard, they were like clouds of poison. He was allergic to those flowers. He knew that if he went outside today, his eyes would swell and his nose would run. He would feel as if he couldn't breathe. He knew, because it had happened to him on Monday, and since that day he had not been able to go out on the field.

At lunch Mr. Hunter told him, "Ms. Gomez is expecting you in the library, Richard. Have fun." Richard nodded sadly. He hoped those trees would stop blooming soon so he could go out with the other kids. He was tired of sitting in the library while everyone else played outside.

Then Luci said, "I'll go with you, if that's OK." Luci was on crutches because she had hurt her foot in a basketball game.

"Do you have to go to the library too?" asked Richard, thinking she couldn't go out because of her injury.

Luci shrugged. "I'd rather go to the library. We'll have all the books to ourselves. There's one about spiders I've been wanting to read, but someone else always gets it first."

Richard knew the book she meant, because everyone had been talking about it. In fact, he'd been wanting to read it too. Maybe the library wasn't so bad after all.

Turn the page.

Answer the questions below.

1 In the simile in the first paragraph, what two things does the author compare?

   A cotton and clouds

   B flowers and milk

   C clouds and poison

   D poison and flowers

2 What did Luci and Richard have in common?

   F Neither one liked to read.

   G Neither one could play outside.

   H Neither one was allergic to spring flowers.

   J Neither one played basketball.

3 How was Luci's attitude different from Richard's?

   A She wanted to go outside.

   B She wanted to be alone.

   C She was glad to go to the library.

   D She didn't like what she saw out the window.

4 In what way were Richard's feelings at the end of the story different from his feelings at the beginning?

_____

_____

_____

_____

5 What happened to change Richard's attitude?

_____

_____

_____

_____

Read the selection. Then answer the questions that follow.

Clocks

Noah inserted the clock key into a hole in the clock face and turned it three times. The clock chimed with a loud *bong*, as it did every hour and every time Noah wound it. His great aunt had carried it when she moved from Russia to the United States decades before. The clock was older than Noah, older even than his parents. It had to be wound every morning or it would stop, and winding it was Noah's responsibility.

He thought about asking his mother if he could move the clock into his room, although he knew it would wake him every time it chimed. "Most of my friends have clocks in their rooms," he hinted.

"This isn't the sort of clock to have in your room," his mother answered. "Most modern clocks don't chime, and they don't need to be wound."

Noah traced the carved wood with his fingers. He was not especially impressed with modern clocks.

Turn the page.

Answer the questions below.

1 How was the old clock different from most modern clocks?

  A It had to be wound.

  B It didn't keep time as well.

  C It came from another country.

  D It was much smaller.

2 In what way were Noah and his great aunt alike?

  F Both of them once lived in Russia.

  G Both wanted to keep the older clock with them.

  H Neither one liked modern clocks.

  J Neither one remembered to wind the clock.

3 Which statement from the story is a generalization?

  A It was older than Noah, even older than his parents.

  B Winding it was Noah's responsibility.

  C Most of my friends have clocks in their rooms.

  D Noah traced the carved wood with his fingers.

4 Would you like a clock like Noah's better than a modern clock? Explain your answer.

_____

_____

_____

_____

_____

_____

_____

_____

_____

_____

Read the selection. Then answer the questions that follow.

Making a Decision

Dear Sis,

How is college? We have all missed you since you moved away from home.

Our big news is that we're going to get a dog. Mom and Dad drove us to the animal shelter yesterday to choose one. Miguel liked a little white dog. Her name is Cotton. She only weighs six pounds, even though she is fully grown. Mom says she is a "lap dog." That means she is a good size for Miguel to hold in his lap. She is too small to spend much time outside, though. Dad says she would be a good watchdog because she barked the whole time we were at the shelter.

My favorite is a puppy named Rex. Rex is already larger than the white dog, even though he's only three months old. He has big floppy ears and thick brown fur. His feet are almost like pancakes. Dad says he'll weigh forty or fifty pounds when he's fully grown. That's OK with me. I want a big dog that I can take running with me in the park.

Most of the dogs we saw yesterday were friendly. I'd be happy to bring any of them home. The real problem is making a decision. What do you think? Should we adopt a sweet little lap dog or a big dog like Rex? Maybe we should get them both!

Anyway, when you come home for summer break you'll meet our new four-footed family member!

Your sister,

Cristina

Turn the page.

Answer the questions below.

1 How are Cotton and Rex alike?

 A Both make good lap dogs.

 B Both are at the animal shelter.

 C Both have large ears and feet.

 D Both weigh forty or fifty pounds.

2 Why are Rex's feet compared to pancakes in the third paragraph?

 F to show the size of his feet

 G to imply that his feet are messy

 H because they both are warm

 J to show the color of his feet

3 Which statement from the letter is a generalization?

 A Mom and Dad drove us to the animal shelter yesterday to choose one.

 B She is too small to spend much time outside, though.

 C Most of the dogs we saw yesterday were friendly.

 D Maybe we should get them both!

4 What answer best completes this chart comparing the two dogs?

Cotton	Rex
6 pounds	40 or 50 pounds
lap dog	outdoor dog
?	still a puppy

 F barks a lot

 G fully grown

 H white coat

 J long hair

5 How are Cristina and Miguel alike, and how are they different? Give at least one example of each.

_____

_____

_____

_____

Read the selection. Then answer the questions that follow.

A Faster Way to Send Messages

If you want to give a message to a friend in another city, you could make a telephone call. If you have a computer, you could send an e-mail.

In the early 1800s, there were no computers, and Alexander Graham Bell had not yet invented the telephone. Most people wrote letters, but mail was slower than it is today. Mail traveled by boat or horseback, so a letter could take a very long time to go from one city to another.

A man named Samuel Morse thought that people should have a faster way to send messages. Morse knew that some scientists had been working to solve this problem, and he began experimenting too. He had heard about machines that sent controlled bursts of electricity over wires. He built a better machine than the other scientists. His machine—the telegraph—sent short and long bursts of electricity over very long wires.

Next, Morse designed a code for sending messages. In his code, the short and long bursts of energy were combined in different ways. Each combination stood for a letter of the alphabet. For example, a short and a long burst stood for the letter A. One long and three short bursts stood for the letter B. With Morse Code, people could send messages over long distances in a short period of time.

There were many changes in communication after Morse's invention. The telegraph caught on, and wires were strung from city to city. People were informed about important news more quickly than ever before. Businesspeople used the telegraph to buy and sell products. People could send messages across the country in minutes, instead of months.

Turn the page.

Answer the questions below.

1 What was one difference between the telegraph and mail in the early 1800s?

A It cost more to send a letter than to use a telegraph.

B There were more telegraph offices than post offices.

C The telegraph was faster than the mail.

D The telegraph traveled by boat while a letter traveled by horseback.

2 What did Alexander Graham Bell and Samuel Morse have in common?

F Both worked on the first telegraph.

G Both invented ways to send messages.

H Both were born in the early 1800s.

J Both started out working for the post office.

3 What statement from the selection is a generalization?

A If you have a computer, you could send an e-mail.

B Most people wrote letters, but mail was slower than it is today.

C Morse knew that some scientists had been trying to solve this problem.

D One long and three short bursts stood for the letter *B*.

4 How would you communicate with a friend in another city, and how would that be different from using a telegraph?

_____

_____

_____

_____

5 In what way was the invention of the telegraph like the invention of the computer?

_____

_____

_____

_____

Read the selection. Then answer the questions that follow.

Distracting Henri

Henri picked up a bright red carton of raisins. Patrick said firmly, "We have raisins at home."

The little boy dropped the carton onto the black conveyor belt that carried their groceries to the cash register. Their father quickly grabbed it while Henri wailed.

Knowing it was the red box that Henri wanted, Patrick glanced about for something to distract his brother. His eye fell on a bin of apples near the door, and he said, "Look at the red apples, Henri." The little boy headed toward the apples. Patrick let him hold one for a moment, then put it back on the pile and handed him another.

Soon, their father arrived, gripping a handful of plastic bags. "Ready to go?"

Patrick took the apple from Henri and saw a bite mark on one side. "Oh no," he groaned.

The boys' father sighed and went back to the cash register to pay for the apple.

Turn the page.

Answer the questions below.

1 What clue from the story tells readers that the story takes place in modern times?

A Henri seemed to like things that were red.

B Henri's father went back and paid for the apple.

C The grocery store had a conveyor belt and plastic bags.

D There were three characters in the story, a father and two boys.

2 What word best describes Patrick?

F athletic

G helpful

H selfish

J forgetful

3 Why did Henri want the box of raisins?

A He was hungry.

B He wanted to make cookies with them.

C He was trying to get his father's attention.

D He liked the red box.

4 Why didn't Patrick stop Henri from biting the apple?

_____

_____

_____

_____

_____

_____

_____

_____

_____

_____

Read the selection. Then answer the questions that follow.

Something Wonderful

When the doorbell rang, Triet looked through the peephole. He saw a delivery person already hurrying down the stairs. She had left a package behind in the hallway. Triet called his brother. "Khai! There's a package in the hall for us! Someone sent us something!"

Khai looked out and then opened the door to retrieve the package. "It's addressed to Mom and Dad," he said. "We can't open it until they wake up."

Triet knew his parents enjoyed sleeping late on weekends. It might be hours before they awoke. He plopped down on the floor beside the package and stared at it. It seemed to come to life, staring back at him and whispering, "You should open me because I'm something wonderful." His hand fell on the taped end, and the paper wrapping loosened a bit.

He eyed the brown paper and wondered what was inside. The return address told him the package had come from his grandparents. Could they have sent him a toy?

A hand fell on his shoulder. "What have you got there?" his mother asked in a sleepy voice.

Triet leapt up and thrust the package at her, saying, "It's for you and Dad, something from Grandfather."

His mother pulled open the end that Triet had loosened. She said, "I know what it is. Remember the delicious cantaloupe Grandfather grew in his garden last summer? Well, this year, we'll grow some that will be just as good."

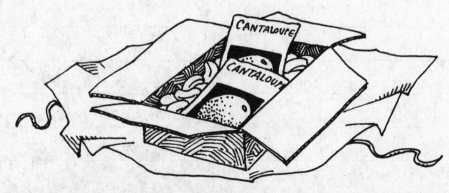

Turn the page.

Answer the questions below.

1 **Where does this story take place?**

   A the farm where Triet's grandfather lives

   B the apartment where Triet and Khai live

   C the hallway where the package was delivered

   D the post office that sent the package

2 **What clue from the story tells readers that the story took place in modern times?**

   F The boys' parents were asleep.

   G Someone brought a package to the door.

   H Triet heard the doorbell ring.

   J Khai told Triet not to open the package.

3 **You can tell from the story that Triet was good at**

   A imagining things.

   B getting along with others.

   C waiting for things to happen.

   D following directions.

4 **What was in the package?**

   F fruit

   G a toy

   H garden tools

   J seeds

5 **What might Triet have done if his mother had not been awake?**

_____

_____

_____

_____

_____

_____

_____

Read the selection. Then answer the questions that follow.

Favorites

Mama, Maggie, and I sat on the porch, snapping the ends off green beans. We tossed the ends into one bucket and the fat middles into another filled with water. It occurred to me that nothing was ever wasted on a farm. The bucketful of ends would be thrown onto a compost pile, where they would rot and turn into fertilizer for Mama's garden. We would eat the middles of the beans of course, and the water would be saved for scrubbing dishes after supper. Later, Maggie and I would sprinkle the water over the tomato vines.

"I like the neatness of farming, the way it all fits together, every single thing being part of every other thing," I said to Mama.

"It's hard work," she replied with a smile.

I answered, "I like it, though."

With a sour look, Maggie said, "You're just saying that because you want to be Mama's favorite." Maggie was always grouchy about something.

This time, she made me so angry I snapped, "You wish you were too! Maybe if you weren't so mean . . ."

Mama gave us an impatient look and said, "I love all my children. I don't have a favorite, for goodness' sake."

I glanced at Maggie and saw fat tears hanging from her eyelashes. I wished now that I hadn't hurt her feelings. I wanted to make it up to her. So when Mama stepped into the yard to shout at the boys, I whispered, "You're Daddy's favorite, and it makes me real mad sometimes too."

Answer the questions below.

1 What did the narrator like about farming?

   A the hard work

   B the way nothing is wasted

   C the chance to spend time with her sister

   D having fresh food such as green beans

2 What sentence best describes the way the sisters got along?

   F Each tried to be better than the other at everything they did.

   G They were usually kind and thoughtful.

   H They disliked one another.

   J They were close but sometimes hurt each other.

3 What tells the reader that the story took place a long time ago?

   A The people are dressed in old-fashioned clothing.

   B The family lives on a farm.

   C People don't grow tomatoes anymore.

   D They put the green beans in metal buckets.

4 Could this same story take place on a modern-day farm? Explain your answer.

_____

_____

_____

_____

5 How do you think Maggie felt at the end of the story? Explain.

_____

_____

_____

_____

_____

Read the selection. Then answer the questions that follow.

The Liberty Bell

The colony of Pennsylvania ordered the Liberty Bell in 1751 and had it shipped from England. On the day it was hung, it cracked. The broken bell was melted down, and the same metal was used to make a new one.

For most Americans, the Liberty Bell is a symbol of freedom. Carved on it are the words "Proclaim Liberty throughout all the land." It rang to call people together the first time the Declaration of Independence was read. For many years after that, the bell rang every Fourth of July. But soon another crack began to develop. By Washington's birthday in 1846 the crack had grown so wide that the bell could no longer be rung.

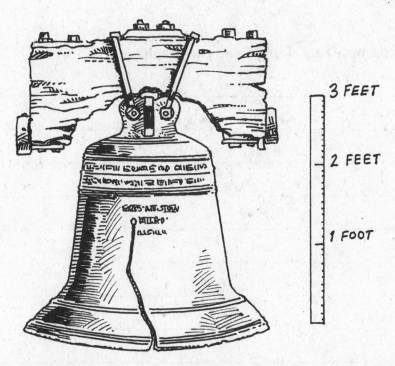

3 FEET

2 FEET

1 FOOT

In the mid-1800s, a crack appeared in the Liberty Bell. For this reason, it is no longer rung. Cracked and silent, the bell is still a symbol of freedom. Today it hangs in Philadelphia, Pennsylvania.

Turn the page.

Answer the questions below.

1 **Where is the Liberty Bell now?**

A Washington, D.C.

B London, England

C Philadelphia, Pennsylvania

D Independence, Missouri

2 **The picture of the Liberty Bell tells you that it is about**

F one foot high.

G two feet high.

H three feet high.

J four feet high.

3 **Which statement about the Liberty Bell is supported by its picture?**

A It is too loud.

B It is cracked.

C It was melted down.

D It came from England.

4 **Which sentence states the main idea of the second paragraph?**

_____

_____

_____

_____

_____

_____

_____

_____

_____

_____

Name _____

Read the selection. Then answer the questions that follow.

The Great Sahara Desert

The great Sahara was not always a desert. A few thousand years ago, farmers were able to grow crops there. The region received more rainfall then, and the soil was rich. Then, over many years, the climate changed. Rain stopped falling, the soil became dry, and the farmers left.

The Sahara Desert's climate is now very dry. In some places, no rain falls for years at a time. As you might expect, days are often blisteringly hot. It may surprise you to learn that nights in the desert can be freezing cold.

Most people think of this desert as having three parts: the rocky western part, the mountains in the middle, and the eastern part, which is the driest. The eastern area is what many people think of when they think of desert. Great hills of sand rise hundreds of feet in the air. These rolling dunes stretch as far as the eye can see.

Humans have lived on the edges of the desert for thousands of years. After the Arabs brought camels to the area, people finally had an animal that could carry them across the desert. But most traders still prefer to earn their livings elsewhere. In general, the Sahara is a harsh and unwelcoming place to living things.

_____ ?

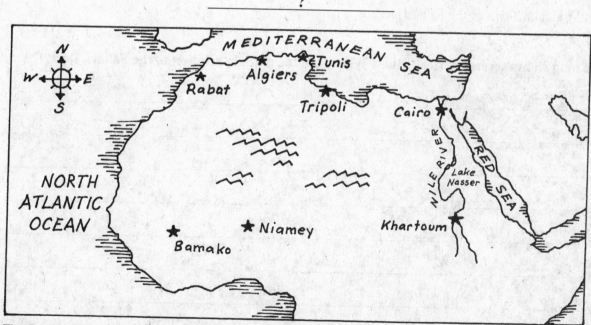

The Sahara covers much of northern Africa, stretching from the Atlantic Ocean to the Red Sea.

Turn the page.

Answer the questions below.

1 What is the main idea in the first paragraph of the selection?

A There were once farms in the Sahara.

B The rain stopped falling.

C The Sahara has changed over time.

D The farmers went somewhere else.

2 On the west, the border of the Sahara Desert is the

F Sea of Nasser.

G Atlantic Ocean.

H Pacific Ocean.

J Red Sea.

3 According to the map, what river runs through the Sahara Desert?

A the Nile River

B the Red River

C the Tripoli River

D the Mediterranean River

4 What is the best title for the map?

F The Eastern Sahara

G The Sahara Desert in Modern Times

H Ancient Farms in the Sahara Desert

J Mountain Trails of the Sahara Desert

5 The map shows several African cities. Where are the cities in relation to the Sahara Desert?

_____

_____

_____

_____

_____

_____

_____

Read the selection. Then answer the questions that follow.

One of the World's Oldest Toys

You slip the loop of string over your finger, and your hand curls around the toy. Your hand flips backward, and the yo-yo rolls down the string. It spins at the end of its string for a fraction of a second and then bounces back up to your hand. Once you start playing with a yo-yo, it's hard to stop.

The word *yo-yo* comes from a country known as the Philippines. It means "come come." Children there have been playing with this type of toy for hundreds of years, although they were not the first. Greek children have had yo-yos for thousands of years. It is one of the world's oldest toys.

_____?_____

1928
Pedro Flores, a Filipino American, opens a yo-yo factory in Santa Barbara, California. Soon he opens two more factories. Flores also starts holding contests. To win, people have to keep their yo-yos spinning up and down for hours without stopping or making any mistakes. The contests draw big crowds. This is when the toy really becomes a hit in this country.

1950s
A new kind of yo-yo becomes popular. This one makes it easier to do tricks, even for beginners.

500 B.C.
An ancient vase shows a child in Greece playing with a yo-yo 2,500 years ago.

1866
Two men, James L. Haven and Charles Hettrich, are issued the first U.S. patent on the yo-yo.

1930
Donald Duncan buys Flores's corporation. Duncan sells even more yo-yos than Flores had. When people think of yo-yos, they think of Duncan.

Turn the page.

Answer the questions below.

1 Greek children have played with yo-yos for at least

   A 2,500 years.

   B 1,000 years.

   C 500 years.

   D 200 years.

2 What happened in the 1950s, according to the time line?

   F Hettrich and Haven received a patent on the yo-yo.

   G Factories started to mass-produce yo-yos.

   H Yo-yo contests became popular.

   J A new type of yo-yo made it easier to do tricks.

3 What would make the best title for the time line?

   A Types of Yo-Yos

   B How to Use a Yo-Yo

   C How a Yo-Yo Is Made

   D The History of Yo-Yos

4 What is the main idea of the second paragraph?

_____

_____

_____

_____

5 According to the time line, who was Pedro Flores and why was he important?

_____

_____

_____

_____

_____

Read the selection. Then answer the questions that follow.

A Prickly Situation

Bart, the cowhand, sometimes walked in his sleep. His buddy, Simms, kept the bunkhouse cleaned up so Bart would not stumble while sleepwalking. Then one day they were on a roundup far from home and had to camp out in the hills.

Bart started snoring as soon as his head hit the bedroll. But he woke up at midnight, standing in his flannel pajamas in the middle of a thicket of prickly pear cactus. Amazingly, there was not a scratch on him!

He shouted for help, and Simms hurried out to see what all the ruckus was about. "How did you get in there without getting poked?" he asked.

Bart grumbled, "I don't know—I was sleeping! How do you reckon I can get out of here?"

Simms said, "Maybe you should go back to sleep."

So Bart curled up on the ground, and at sunup he awoke safe and sound in his own bedroll.

Turn the page.

Answer the questions below.

1 What was Bart's main problem in the story?

  A The bunkhouse was too clean.

  B Simms was never around when Bart needed him.

  C He was afraid of sleeping outside.

  D He sleepwalked into a cactus patch.

2 What did Bart do when he woke up in the cactus patch?

  F He called Simms.

  G He stepped over the cactus.

  H He looked for the trail.

  J He told Simms to stop shouting.

3 What is one thing Bart did to resolve his problem?

  A He woke up at midnight.

  B He kept the bunkhouse cleaned up.

  C He asked Simms what to do.

  D He camped out in the hills.

4 How were Bart and Simms alike, and how were they different?

_____

_____

_____

_____

_____

_____

_____

_____

_____

_____

Read the selection. Then answer the questions that follow.

The Flag

When Mr. Brown announced that they would make a class flag, no one suspected that it would turn out to be so difficult. Ann said she knew exactly what it should look like: white stars on a purple background. Some of the others laughed. That was the first clue that it might not be easy to find an idea the whole class would like.

All the classes were making flags. Mr. Brown reminded his students that each flag was supposed to tell something about the students in the class. A purple flag with white stars would say nothing about the students in Mr. Brown's class.

Luis suggested, "Katie and I play soccer, and so does Tran. How about a green background with a soccer ball on it?"

"What about the rest of the class?" Mr. Brown reminded him. "Max plays baseball, Rachel plays basketball, and some students aren't interested in sports."

"Everyone likes music, don't they?" offered Rachel. "How about a black musical note on a white background?"

Tran shook his head. "I like music, but I don't think a musical note tells anything about me."

Katie's eyes were thoughtful as she said, "There are nineteen of us in this class."

"So?" asked Mario. "You think we should put a number on our flag?"

"No," said Katie. "The main thing we all have in common is that we are all different. What if we put nineteen kids on the flag, with no two kids exactly the same?"

Katie's suggestion pleased everyone, but Luis still had one question. "What color should the background be?"

"Brown, naturally!" replied Mr. Brown, with a comical grin.

Turn the page.

Answer the questions below.

1 What was the problem Mr. Brown's class had to solve?

  A how to choose colors for a class flag

  B how to make a flag that represented the whole class

  C how to agree on something when everyone had a different idea

  D how to make a decision when everyone wanted to talk at once

2 Which of the following was part of the rising action?

  F Ann suggested white stars on a purple background.

  G Katie's suggestion pleased everyone.

  H Mr. Brown knew what color the background should be.

  J Luis still had one question.

3 What was wrong with both Ann's and Luis's suggestions?

  A Neither suggested colors that everyone liked.

  B Neither showed a sport or a musical note.

  C Neither was an idea that would look good on a flag.

  D Neither said something about everyone in the class.

4 How did Katie's suggestion resolve the problem?

  F It showed both a soccer ball and a musical note.

  G It met with Mr. Brown's approval.

  H It showed something about the class.

  J It showed most of the class.

5 What did Katie see about the class that helped to solve the problem?

_____

_____

_____

_____

_____

_____

Read the selection. Then answer the questions that follow.

Easy As Pie

The truck rattled to a stop beside a sign that read Downtown Bus. Mr. Aguilar said, "Meet me back here at four o'clock." Will and his grandmother scrambled out, slammed the door, and waved as Mr. Aguilar drove away.

Grandmother pulled a map out of her capacious handbag and pointed. "We'll take this bus downtown and get off at the county courthouse. Easy as pie."

Will was excited about visiting the city and wanted to experience everything. He was even excited about riding the bus. He lived with his grandmother in the small town of Farrell, where a person could stroll from one end of town to the other in ten minutes.

When the bus arrived, they got in line behind a man with hair that spiked out in all directions. He fed a dollar bill into a box beside the driver. Grandmother attempted to stuff a folded-up dollar bill into the slot, which caused the driver to mutter something under his breath. She unfolded the bill and it slipped right in.

Once they were seated, she kept glancing from her map to the window. "What's wrong?" asked Will.

"These street names don't look familiar," worried Grandmother. "I'm afraid we've taken the wrong bus."

Will studied the map and said, "I don't think you're looking at the right part of the map. Aren't we really here?" He pointed.

Grandmother nodded sharply. "Smart boy. Now I wonder how we get this bus to stop."

Will suddenly realized that his grandmother had never ridden a city bus either. They were passing the courthouse! What should they do?

The spiky-haired man smiled from across the aisle. "This bus always stops at the next corner," he said.

Will sighed with relief.

"Easy as pie," said Grandmother.

Turn the page.

Answer the questions below.

1 What was the first problem Will and Grandmother had?

A getting on the wrong bus

B putting money in the box

C getting off at the wrong stop

D not knowing how to stop the bus

2 What event from the story is an example of rising action?

F Grandmother saying they might be on the wrong bus

G Will being excited about his visit to the city

H Grandmother and Will getting off the bus

J Mr. Aguilar dropping them off at the bus stop

3 What was the climax of the story?

A He lived with his grandmother in the small town of Farrell.

B She kept glancing from her map to the window.

C They were passing the courthouse! What should they do?

D "Easy as pie," said Grandmother.

4 How were Will's feelings at the beginning of the story different from his feelings at the end?

_____

_____

_____

_____

_____

5 What was the resolution of the problem in this story?

_____

_____

_____

_____

_____

Read the selection. Then answer the questions that follow.

Would You Like Your Salad With Worms, or Without?

"There's a worm on my salad," Olympia said. Mike peered at the wriggling, green worm. Mama made a *tsk* sound as she took the salad away.

Olympia and her brother had been doing chores all morning, and she was hungry. "I'll eat that one," she said. "I just don't want the worm."

Mike snickered. Mama made a little *o* with her mouth and tossed the salad into a bucket for the hogs to eat later.

Olympia's stomach growled. After what seemed like a long time, Mama set a fresh salad down. The new lettuce looked clean and fresh, but a ladybug walked out from beneath a leaf. Mike saw it and started to speak, but Olympia shook her head. She let the ladybug walk onto her fork, and then flicked it to the floor. Quickly, she ate her salad.

Turn the page.

Answer the questions below.

1 Why did the author begin the story with the sentence, "There's a worm on my salad"?

   A to introduce the theme of the story

   B to make the story sound serious

   C to tell readers the story takes place on a farm

   D to grab the readers' attention quickly

2 What did Olympia do after seeing the ladybug?

   F She told her mother about it.

   G She removed it and ate the salad anyway.

   H She tossed out the salad immediately.

   J She gave it to her brother.

3 What was the main reason the author wrote this story?

   A to describe life on a family farm

   B to give facts about eating fresh vegetables

   C to entertain readers with a story about a very hungry girl

   D to persuade readers that insects and worms are harmless

4 "Would You Like Your Salad With Worms, or Without?" is an unusual title. Why do you think the author chose it?

_____

_____

_____

_____

_____

_____

_____

_____

_____

Read the selection. Then answer the questions that follow.

The Old Bookstore

As I stand on the corner of Eighth Street and Walnut Avenue, a glass skyscraper towers overhead. Its shadow is deep and cool. It's an impressive building, but I remember something better.

I've lived in this neighborhood all my life, and I remember when a bookstore stood here. The front of the store was painted blue. A bell jingled when my friends and I shoved open the door. Inside, the air smelled like books and chocolate chip cookies. The display window always held an electric fan that blew that cookie-and-book smell into the street.

The fan was the only fast-moving thing in the place. A black-haired woman and her tall husband sat on stools behind the counter, reading. "How about a cookie?" the woman always offered us, smiling and pointing to a glass platter on the counter.

On Saturdays, there were storytellers in costumes of scientists, astronauts, or farmers. They stood in the middle of the shop spinning tales, and I sprawled on the floor with my friends, listening. It was the best way to spend a Saturday morning— better than cartoons, better than sleeping late.

This tall building, reflecting blue sky in its glass, is here now. This part of town has always been busy, an area where everything always moved fast. Cars zipped around this corner. Buses roared down the street. That's why the old bookstore was so great. It slowed life down for us, almost like something out of a science fiction novel.

Turn the page.

Answer the questions below.

1 What words in paragraph 2 tell the reader that the bookstore was there before the skyscraper?

A I've lived in this neighborhood

B I remember when a bookstore stood here

C my friends and I shoved open the door

D The front of the store was painted blue.

2 Why did the author describe how the store smelled?

F to explain why the bookstore closed

G to encourage readers to visit a bookstore

H to make readers laugh at the idea

J to make the store seem more appealing

3 The author probably chose the title "The Old Bookstore" because the story is mostly about

A the importance of reading.

B the smell of cookies.

C a part of the past.

D a busy street.

4 What was the main reason the author wrote this story?

F to share a pleasant memory

G to tell where the skyscraper stood

H to entertain readers with a funny story

J to convince readers to buy books

5 Why did the author include a description of the skyscraper?

_____

_____

_____

_____

_____

_____

_____

_____

Read the selection. Then answer the questions that follow.

The White House

Home of the President

The White House has survived fire, war, and more than two hundred years of use. John Adams was the first President to live there. In 1800, he and his wife moved in before the building was even finished. Work went on all around them.

Destroyed by Fire

During the War of 1812, the White House was burned by British troops. Some people thought it should be replaced with a new building, but President James Madison wanted the White House to remain unchanged. He wanted Americans to know their government was still strong. Since the outside walls were mostly still standing, the White House was rebuilt on the inside. Few changes were made to the outside.

The West Wing

In 1901, Theodore Roosevelt moved in with his wife and six children. At that time, the second floor held offices and living quarters for the First Family. The large Roosevelt family needed more room, so a new wing was built to hold offices. On the second floor of the old White House, the Roosevelt family slept, played with their many pets, and did homework.

Much Needed Repairs

By the time Harry Truman was elected President in 1945, the nearly 150-year-old White House desperately needed repairs. In fact, the President felt that the entire inside should be torn out and rebuilt. President Truman and his family lived in a building across the street, while bulldozers dug out a new basement for the White House. Air conditioning and heating equipment were added, as well as fire protection. Four years later, a new White House stood inside those old, old walls.

© Pearson Education 4

Turn the page.

Answer the questions below.

1 The inside of the White House has been rebuilt twice. What was the reason the first time?

A A fire had destroyed the inside.

B President Adams needed more office space.

C The Roosevelt family needed more living space.

D The building contained poor quality materials.

2 Why did the author include paragraph headings in this selection?

F to show the reader when important events happened

G to let the reader know what each section is about

H to convince the reader that the author knows about the White House

J to encourage the reader to read more slowly

3 What is the most likely reason the author wrote this selection?

A to entertain readers with a sad story

B to express love for the United States

C to encourage readers to study history

D to present facts about the White House

4 In more than two hundred years much has happened at the White House. Why did the author choose to include only these four events?

_____

_____

_____

_____

5 Why do you think the author organized information in chronological order?

_____

_____

_____

_____

Read the selection. Then answer the questions that follow.

All About Peanuts

Are peanuts food? Well, just like many meats, they are packed with calories and protein. Some people eat them roasted, right out of the shell, while others make cookies, bread, or pasta with them. For many children in the United States, peanut butter sandwiches are a favorite lunchtime food.

Have you ever wondered how peanut butter is made? First, the outer shells are removed, leaving only the seeds—this is the part of the peanut that we eat. These seeds are roasted and cooled, and then blanched. Blanching is a process that gets rid of a paperlike layer that covers the peanut seeds. After that, they are cleaned, sorted, and ground into peanut butter. Finally, most manufacturers add flavoring, such as a little sugar or salt.

Turn the page.

Answer the questions below.

1 What clue words in the following sentence tell the reader that peanuts and meat are similar?
"Just like many meats, they are packed with calories and protein."

   A Just like

   B they are

   C packed with

   D calories and protein

2 According to the selection, what do cookies, bread, and pasta have in common?

   F They are all good for you.

   G They can all be made with peanuts.

   H Everyone likes them.

   J People eat all of them on sandwiches.

3 What is the first step in making peanut butter?

   A cleaning the peanuts

   B cooking the seeds

   C getting rid of the shells

   D grinding the seeds

4 Think of another food that is used in sandwiches. How is it the same or different from peanut butter?

_____

_____

_____

_____

_____

_____

_____

_____

Read the selection. Then answer the questions that follow.

Tortoises Are Turtles

From head to tail, the Galapagos tortoise is about as long as you are tall. However, it weighs far more—somewhere around five hundred pounds, or as much as three grown men! It lives on only a few islands in the Pacific Ocean, and it is one of the largest tortoises.

The speckled tortoise of Africa is a cousin of the monstrous Galapagos. One of the smallest tortoises, this one is so tiny you could hold it in one hand.

Tortoises are a family of turtles that live on land. There are about forty different kinds, but only three of these live in the United States. Tortoises look a little different than other turtles because most tortoises have shells that are taller and more rounded. Their legs and feet are shaped differently too. Many turtles have webbed feet or even flippers, to make it easier for them to move around in water. Tortoises have legs that are thick and round, like a tree trunk.

Tortoises, just like other turtles, are reptiles and hatch from eggs. A mother turtle digs a hole and lays her eggs inside it. She covers the eggs with soil, and then leaves. The soil protects the eggs and keeps them warm. When the turtles hatch, they dig to the surface and take care of themselves. Most young turtles do not survive, but those that do may live to a ripe old age. Some have lived to be more than one hundred years old!

Turn the page.

Answer the questions below.

1 What two things does the author compare in the first sentence?

 A a tortoise and a person

 B an ocean and a tortoise

 C a man and a child

 D a tortoise and an island

2 What clue words in the following sentence show that tortoises are similar to other turtles?

 "Tortoises, just like other turtles, are reptiles and hatch from eggs."

 F just like

 G other turtles

 H are reptiles

 J hatch from eggs

3 What happens after turtle eggs hatch?

 A The mother turtle digs a nest.

 B The soil warms them.

 C The young turtles dig their way out.

 D The mother turtle leaves.

4 What is one way in which tortoises are different from other turtles?

 F Tortoises are reptiles and most turtles are not.

 G Tortoises' shells are not shaped like other turtles'.

 H Tortoises are smaller than most other turtles.

 J Tortoises spend more time in the water than turtles.

5 Choose another animal that you know something about. Explain how the tortoise is like that animal, and how it is different.

_____

_____

_____

_____

_____

_____

Read the selection. Then answer the questions that follow.

Marshes, Swamps, and Bogs

Imagine a place where water covers the land for most of the year. Perhaps this place lies on the edge of a river, lake, or ocean. Maybe it is just a low, flat spot on the Earth's surface, a place where water does not drain away. What all of these places have in common is that the land is wet most of the time. That is why they're called "wetlands."

Marshes, swamps, and bogs are all wetlands. Marshes are covered with grasses and reeds—few bushes or trees grow there. They are found in warm and cold climates, on the edges of rivers, lakes, or oceans. Swamps are found in these places too. The biggest difference is that many trees and bushes grow in swamps. Both marshes and swamps are home to many animals, plants, and insects.

Bogs are usually found in very cold places. They form on low, flat land where water does not drain away. A bog starts to form when parts of plants fall into the water. The plants begin to fall apart but don't completely decay. This means they don't rot and turn into soil. Instead, they pile up in a soft layer called "peat." For a time, the layer of peat floats in the water, like a raft. Then, as years pass, it becomes very thick, in some places as deep as a house is tall. Small bushes and mosses grow on top of it.

Many insects and a number of plants live in bogs, as well as birds, frogs, and some other small animals. However, they do not usually have as many animals as swamps and marshes.

Turn the page.

Answer the questions below.

1 What clue word in the following sentence tells readers that swamps and marshes are similar?
"**Both marshes and swamps are home to many animals, plants, and insects.**"

A Both

B home

C many

D and

2 What is being compared to the size of a house in the third paragraph?

F marsh plants

G swamp trees

H rotting soil

J floating peat

3 What is the main difference between swamps and marshes?

A Marshes are home to insects, and swamps are not.

B Only swamps are filled with peat.

C Swamps have many trees, and marshes do not.

D Only marshes are covered with water all the time.

4 Describe what happens when a bog is formed.

_____

_____

_____

_____

5 Write two ways in which swamps, marshes, and bogs are all similar.

_____

_____

_____

_____

Read the selection. Then answer the questions that follow.

Bringing Rana Home

As soon as the Silvas returned from their vacation, Alonso pleaded with his mother to pick up Rana, the family's Labrador retriever. The dog had stayed with another family while the Silvas were on vacation, and Alonso could hardly wait to see her. Mrs. Silva telephoned their friends and asked if they could pick up Rana.

When the door opened, Rana rushed out and threw herself at Alonso. He and his mother laughed and thanked their friends for caring for the dog.

At first, Rana rode in the front seat of the car, her head hanging out of the window. She barked at everyone they passed, as if to exclaim, "My family has returned, after all! Isn't it wonderful?"

Mrs. Silva soon grew tired of Rana's barking and rolled up the window, despite whimpers from the dog. Alonso slapped his hands on his thighs and said, "Come sit in back with me, Rana." She went to him, her brown eyes full of gladness.

Turn the page.

Answer the questions below.

1 What clue words in the first paragraph tell the reader when Alonso wanted to pick up Rana?

   A As soon as the Silvas returned

   B the family's Labrador retriever

   C The dog had stayed with another family

   D asked if they could pick up Rana

2 Which of these happened first in the story?

   F Rana sat in the back seat.

   G Mrs. Silva called their friends.

   H Alonso and Rana sat together.

   J Rana jumped on Alonso.

3 What did Rana do after Mrs. Silva rolled up the window?

   A She sat in the front seat.

   B She ran out the door.

   C She barked at people.

   D She whimpered.

4 Do you think Alonso missed Rana while his family was on vacation?

_____

_____

_____

_____

_____

_____

_____

_____

_____

_____

_____

Read the selection. Then answer the questions that follow.

The Race

The children lined up in the middle of the dirt road. Jesse, the oldest, stood on the far side, leaning forward. Beside him, Thomas stuffed a paperback book into the pocket of his pants. Next came Mary, tall and relaxed, only an inch or two shorter than Jesse. Ruthie was on the end. She studied the row of bare feet in the dust. They were all bigger than hers, all fidgety and itching to run.

Ruthie counted, "One, two, three, go!" A spatter of gravel and dust flew out behind Jesse as he took off running, leaving the others behind. Mary's muscular legs carried her away too, and even Thomas showed Ruthie his back. She didn't mind. She was glad to be racing with her older cousins—there was never any thought that she would win.

Thomas soon slowed to a walk, holding his side with one hand. Ruthie caught up and walked with him. Jesse reached the pine tree at the bend in the road, touched its trunk, and started back. Seconds later, Mary did the same. They sprinted toward Thomas and Ruthie, who stopped to watch.

Ruthie remembered that Mary had insisted the race must be to the tree and back. "That's a long way to run," Jesse had said.

Mary had replied, "Maybe you can run faster, but I can run farther."

Thomas had laughed, not really believing her.

As Ruthie and Thomas watched, Mary proved it. Barely ahead of Mary, Jesse struggled up to the younger cousins. In that moment, Mary lowered her chin and smiled. Her feet pounded the dusty road, making a soft sound: *slap, slap, slap, slap.* She ran by with a wink for Ruthie and passed Jesse without even breathing hard.

Turn the page.

Answer the questions below.

1 What clue words in the second paragraph tell the reader who started running first?
- **A** Ruthie counted
- **B** leaving the others behind
- **C** carried her away
- **D** never any thought

2 Who reached the pine tree first?
- **F** Ruthie
- **G** Thomas
- **H** Mary
- **J** Jesse

3 What did Ruthie and Thomas do as Jesse and Mary turned and ran toward them?
- **A** They slowed down.
- **B** They ran as fast as they could.
- **C** They stopped.
- **D** They lined up across the road.

4 When did Mary say she could run farther than Jesse?
- **F** before the race
- **G** when they started running
- **H** when she passed Jesse
- **J** after the race was over

5 Why did Mary smile at Ruthie and Thomas just before she passed Jesse?

_____

_____

_____

_____

_____

_____

_____

_____

Read the selection. Then answer the questions that follow.

Paper Money

About eight hundred years ago, an Italian boy named Marco Polo traveled to China with his father and uncle. The boy was amazed to see Chinese people trading bits of paper for things of value, such as clothing and food. Years later, he wrote a book about his travels. In his book, he described China's paper money. The people of Europe read Polo's book, but they were used to trading with gold, silver, and other things of clear value. The idea of using paper money did not catch on there for another four hundred years.

In the 1600s, some banks in Europe did begin making paper money. At first, there were problems with people making fake money. To solve this problem, banks began using watermarks. A watermark is a special kind of picture, one that is hard to copy.

Paper for money is made by pouring a liquid mixed with plant fibers over a wire screen. The liquid runs off, leaving a thin layer of fibers on the screen. This layer dries and becomes paper. If a picture is pressed on the screen ahead of time, some parts of the paper are thinner than others. When you hold it up, more light shines through the thin parts. You can see the watermark picture.

Today, most countries of the world use paper money. Each country has its own kind—in the United States, we use dollars. However, computers may be changing all that. Already, huge amounts of money are traded electronically with no paper money at all.

Turn the page.

Answer the questions below.

1 Approximately when did Marco Polo see people using paper money?

  A eight hundred years ago

  B six hundred years ago

  C four hundred years ago

  D two hundred years ago

2 What clue words in the first paragraph tell readers that Marco Polo wrote his book after going to China?

  F traveled to China

  G things of value

  H years later

  J another four hundred years

3 Which of the following is an example of the most recent development in buying and selling?

  A exchanging valuable metals for products

  B trading money by computer

  C paying for goods with paper money

  D swapping labor for crops

4 What events led to the use of watermarks on money?

_____

_____

_____

_____

_____

5 Do you think paper money is better than gold or silver? Give details from the selection or your own experience to support your answer.

_____

_____

_____

_____

_____

Read the selection. Then answer the questions that follow.

Science Class Studies Litter Problem

Roadsides around here are much cleaner this week than last. We can thank fourth-grade students at Wells Creek School and their science teacher, Diana Paz. These students spent most of last Saturday and Sunday collecting roadside trash.

The cleanup is part of a project the class is working on. These students want to know how much litter drivers in this area throw out on the road each month. Students will work one weekend out of every month until the end of the school year. They will gather trash in plastic bags and weigh it. Last weekend, students collected more than one hundred pounds of trash!

Ten parents helped the hardworking students. Some of those parents will not be able to help next month. More volunteers will be needed. If you are able to take part, call Wells Creek School and ask for Ms. Paz.

Turn the page.

Answer the questions below.

1 **What is the main idea of the last paragraph?**

A Ten parents helped the hardworking students.

B Some of those parents will not be able to help next month.

C More volunteers will be needed.

D If you are able to take part, call Wells Creek School and ask for Ms. Paz.

2 **What conclusion can readers draw about Ms. Paz and her students?**

F They believed litter was an important problem.

G They often threw litter on the ground.

H They worked hard every weekend.

J They took part in many science projects.

3 **When did the students collect roadside trash?**

A every day before school

B during science class

C every weekend

D one weekend every month

4 **Write the main idea of the selection and at least one detail that supports it.**

_____

_____

_____

_____

_____

_____

_____

_____

_____

_____

Read the selection. Then answer the questions that follow.

Catch a Wave

You feel the sun's warmth on your back. The surfboard under your belly is warm too. You paddle out toward deeper water. Saltwater splashes in your eyes. You hear the ocean's roar. You reach a place where whitecaps form on the tops of waves. You paddle farther. Finally, you are there, outside of the breaking waves.

The Ride

It's time to catch a wave. One comes toward you, and it's big. You paddle ahead of it back toward shore. The wave lifts your board high in the air. You stand up on your board. You use your feet to balance. You move back a little and use your arms. That's better. This is what it means to catch a wave.

You're flying across the face of a wave that is huge—taller than you. Your surfboard slices into the water like a great knife. You taste salt in your mouth, and something else too. You taste excitement!

The Board

Things have changed since the first British explorers reported seeing Hawaiians surfing. Those Hawaiians used wooden boards. Most of today's surfboards are made of plastic foam covered with a hard shell. Many surfers use "shortboards" because they are fast and easier to maneuver. Other surfers prefer "longboards," which are more than seven feet long.

For that matter, you don't have to use a board to surf. Many surfers ride the waves without boards—it's called *bodysurfing*. It isn't the board that matters most. It's the ride.

Turn the page.

Answer the questions below.

1 What sentence from the selection tells the main idea of the section subtitled "The Ride"?

A It's time to catch a wave.

B One comes toward you, and it's big.

C You stand up on your board.

D You use your feet to balance.

2 According to the selection, what does a surfer do when a big wave is coming?

F sits very still

G stands up quickly

H swims past it

J paddles ahead of it

3 What is the selection mostly about?

A British explorers

B Hawaii

C surfing

D ocean swimming

4 According to the selection, which of the following is true?

F The author of the selection invented surfing.

G Surfboards come in different shapes and sizes.

H Surfing is the most popular sport in Hawaii.

J Most surfboards are made of wood.

5 How does the title support the main idea of the selection?

_____

_____

_____

_____

_____

_____

_____

Read the selection. Then answer the questions that follow.

Feeling Bad?

Everyone experiences it sometime. Your legs feel weak, you are tired, and you have no energy. Perhaps your head hurts. You feel cold, and no matter what you do, you can't warm up. However, the school nurse feels your forehead, says it's hot, and then checks your temperature. It is one hundred and two. You have a fever.

Fever is an increase in body temperature. For most people, normal body temperature is between ninety-eight and ninety-nine degrees Fahrenheit. It can rise if a person sits for a while in a very hot place, such as a sauna. If it does, the brain tells the body to sweat. The person feels the need to go someplace cool. These responses help the body cool itself. Body temperature can also rise when a person is sick.

Fever is not a sickness. It is how the body responds to sickness or sometimes an injury. When a virus enters the body, the brain knows it is there. It tries to fight it off. Experts believe that fever speeds up the body's reaction to the virus. The same thing can happen because of an allergy, infection, or poison.

Fever can be dangerous if it rises too high, so we usually try to get rid of it. One way to do this is to relax in a cool bath. Certain kinds of medicine are also sometimes helpful. A nurse or doctor can help you and your family know the best way to handle a fever.

Turn the page.

Answer the questions below.

1 What sentence in the second paragraph states the paragraph's main idea?

  A Fever is an increase in body temperature.

  B It can rise if a person sits for a while in a very hot place, such as a sauna.

  C The person feels the need to go someplace cool.

  D Body temperature can also rise when a person is sick.

2 According to the selection, what is one reason fever happens?

  F sweating

  G illness

  H lost energy

  J cold weather

3 What is the selection about?

  A virus

  B doctors

  C fever

  D medicine

4 What two things does the school nurse do to conclude that you have a fever?

_____

_____

_____

_____

_____

5 Write the main idea of the last paragraph, and give at least one detail that supports it.

_____

_____

_____

_____

_____

Read the selection. Then answer the questions that follow.

Mrs. Woodruff's Tortoise

A tortoise lived in Mrs. Woodruff's garden. It was fond of vegetables, and Mrs. Woodruff was happy to let it have some. After all, it ate very little.

One day, Mrs. Woodruff came out and discovered the tortoise sadly observing a row of lettuce nubs. The entire row of lettuce had been eaten. She angrily scooped up the tortoise to banish it from her garden. "How could you steal my lettuce after I trusted you to take only what you needed?"

The tortoise just ducked its head into its shell.

Mrs. Woodruff heard her own words, though. She realized that she really had trusted the tortoise because it had never taken more than a little bit. Some other creature must have been in her garden. She gently set down the tortoise inside the garden fence, glad that she had thought things through.

Turn the page.

Answer the questions below.

1 Why did Mrs. Woodruff let the tortoise live in her garden?

  A She thought that tortoises did not eat plants.

  B It only ate weeds and other plants she did not want.

  C She knew it would never eat much.

  D She wanted it to chase away other animals.

2 What did Mrs. Woodruff think when she first saw that the lettuce had been eaten?

  F The tortoise had eaten the lettuce.

  G The lettuce wasn't growing very fast.

  H The lettuce had died.

  J She had picked it herself and forgotten.

3 What is the story's theme?

  A Never trust anyone.

  B Always think before you act.

  C Be kind to animals.

  D Don't take more than you need.

4 Do you think it was a good idea to put the tortoise back in the garden?

_____

_____

_____

_____

_____

_____

_____

_____

_____

_____

_____

© Pearson Education 4

Read the selection. Then answer the questions that follow.

The House

When Carrie's family moved into the Samuels' old house, it was in pretty bad shape. Inside the house, wallpaper sagged off the wall in wide strips. The kitchen stove did not work, and the window was broken. The front steps were downright scary. So many boards were missing that she could see the ground underneath. Carrie said to her mother, "Do we have to live in this house? It's a disaster."

Carrie's mother only smiled and said, "We can put it together. All it needs is a little TLC."

Carrie knew that TLC stood for "tender, loving care." What she didn't understand was why her mother couldn't see that the house needed more than that. It needed a wrecking ball.

Still, she helped her mom repair the broken window in the kitchen. When a truck rolled up with a new stove, Carrie helped move the old one out of the way. She helped her mother pull off the peeling wallpaper. Then, she helped paint the living room walls a bright, happy yellow. Fixing the steps was a big job. Carrie's mother borrowed an electric saw from a friend. Then, she borrowed the friend to help her use it. Carrie helped, too, measuring and holding boards in place while the friend hammered and sawed.

When the steps were repaired, Carrie ran up and down, laughing. "Look at this!" she shouted. "This house is not so bad after all."

Her mother only smiled and said, "All it needed was a little TLC."

Turn the page.

Answer the questions below.

1 The words Carrie uses to describe the house suggest that

A a new kitchen was needed.

B a few repairs were needed.

C it needed cleaning.

D it needed to be torn down.

2 How did Carrie feel about moving into the house?

F unhappy

G excited

H proud

J embarrassed

3 Which of the following best describes Carrie's mother?

A bossy

B lazy

C hardworking

D softhearted

4 What did Carrie learn in the story?

F Everything looks better when it's painted yellow.

G A lot can be done if you're willing to work hard.

H Family is the most important thing.

J You should always measure carefully.

5 How did Carrie feel after the steps were fixed? Give details from the story to support your answer.

_____

_____

_____

_____

_____

_____

_____

Read the selection. Then answer the questions that follow.

The Apple Does Not Roll Far

Wai Ling's great-grandfather had been a famous maker of clay pottery. His name was mentioned in many books, and his clay pots and bowls could be found in museums.

The family possessed only one of the great-grandfather's bowls. It rested on a high shelf, a king of bowls. Wai Ling often stared at it, admiring the strong shape and delicate colors, and wished that she could make something just as lovely.

Her parents knew of her wish and gave her a box of clay. She tried to mold it into a bowl with a strong shape, like her great-grandfather's bowl. When it was finished, she didn't like looking at it. Making bowls was harder than she had thought.

Her father saw it and said, "The apple does not roll far from the tree."

He meant that she was like her great-grandfather, a maker of fine clay pottery. Wai Ling rolled her eyes, certain that he only liked it because he was her father. She stepped in front of the bowl so he could not see it.

Her father took down the great-grandfather's bowl, and Wai Ling touched it, gingerly. The clay was grainy and the color was hard to name because it changed in the light. Sometimes it was a deep reddish-brown, sometimes green like moss growing next to a river.

Her father said, "He made this bowl when he was eighty-seven. He had spent his whole life learning to make it. Do you think his first bowl was like this?"

Wai Ling shook her head. She knew that a person did not learn to make something so special in one afternoon—it would take a lifetime.

Turn the page.

Answer the questions below.

1 What did Wai Ling expect would happen when her parents gave her the clay?

  A She expected to spend her life learning how to make bowls.

  B She thought her parents would show her how to use it.

  C She was afraid to try to make anything with it.

  D She thought she would make a beautiful bowl.

2 What did Wai Ling's father mean when he said, "The apple does not roll far from the tree"?

  F He wanted to put the bowl on the shelf.

  G He wanted to put apples in the bowl.

  H He thought she had her great-grandfather's talent.

  J He thought she should begin by making fruit.

3 How did Wai Ling feel about her bowl at first?

  A She liked the colors.

  B She felt disappointed.

  C She wanted to show it to her father at once.

  D She thought it was too much like her great-grandfather's bowl.

4 What did Wai Ling learn by touching and looking closely at the old bowl?

_____

_____

_____

_____

5 What is the theme of the story? Give at least one detail from the story to support your answer.

_____

_____

_____

_____

_____

Read the selection. Then answer the questions that follow.

Beetles

There are an awful lot of beetles on this Earth. In fact, there are more than 300,000 different kinds—that we know about.

Ladybugs are one kind of beetle that people enjoy having around. Gardeners like them because they eat plant-eating insects. Some people even buy boxes of ladybugs to set free in their gardens.

Not all beetles are good neighbors, though. The boll weevil beetle destroys cotton crops in many parts of the world. Then there is the Japanese beetle—it eats the leaves of plants, causing the plants to die.

In certain tropical areas, beetles grow to be larger than your hand. They have wide, fanlike antennae. Their wings glitter in wonderful shades of blue and green. They are prized by people who collect beetles. That's right—some people collect beetles, and they pay hundreds of dollars for very special ones.

Turn the page.

Answer the questions below.

1 Why do some people release ladybugs in their gardens?

   A They are the most beautiful bugs.

   B Their bright color frightens away beetles.

   C They eat harmful insects.

   D They bring fireflies to the gardens.

2 What happens when Japanese beetles attack plants?

   F The beetles grow larger than your hand.

   G The beetles become good neighbors.

   H The plants turn yellow but are still healthy.

   J The beetles eat the leaves, killing the plants.

3 Which of the following is a statement of opinion?

   A Their wings glitter in wonderful shades of blue and green.

   B Some people even buy boxes of ladybugs and set them free in their gardens.

   C The boll weevil beetle destroys cotton crops in many parts of the world.

   D In certain tropical areas, beetles grow to be larger than your hand.

4 What do you think would happen if everyone started collecting beetles?

_____

_____

_____

_____

_____

_____

_____

_____

_____

_____

_____

Read the selection. Then answer the questions that follow.

Water Expert Comes to Sage City!

Clear, cold water tumbling down a mountain stream is a beautiful sound. On a hot summer day, when throats are scratchy and dry, water tastes better than anything. When rain has not fallen for two months, when our skin is cracking and grass is turning brown, raindrops on our face feel better than anything in the world. Water is important stuff.

Author Wyatt Cameron wants people to think about that, and he's coming to Sage City to tell us how. His latest book, *Don't Waste Our Water,* is about using water wisely. Many of his ideas are simple: Set out barrels in your garden to catch rainwater, and then use it to water your crops. If you must have a lawn, you should plant grass that grows naturally in your area. It will need less water to survive. To wash your car, pour water in a bucket instead of letting the hose run over the car. *Don't Waste Our Water* also has ideas for farmers, ranchers, and city governments.

As most readers know, the Sage City area has had very little rainfall over the past three years. Piney Creek, which supplies many ranches and farms, carries about half as much water as it did five years ago. Wells are drying up. Crops are dying. Ranchers have had to sell off cattle. It's time to make some changes.

If you want to know more about saving water, come to Sage City Hall this Saturday at noon. Wyatt Cameron will be there to sign books and teach us all a thing or two about saving water. Come on out and listen. You'll be glad you did!

Turn the page.

Answer the questions below.

1 According to the selection, if people put water in a bucket to wash cars

  A they will use less water.

  B it will be less messy.

  C they will get the car cleaner.

  D it will take less time.

2 What happened to cause wells to dry up?

  F Farmers and ranchers used too much water.

  G The wells were dug in the wrong places.

  H People in town used too much water.

  J There hadn't been enough rain.

3 Which of the following is a statement of fact?

  A Clear, cold water tumbling down a mountain stream is a beautiful sound.

  B If you must have a lawn, you should plant grass that grows naturally in your area.

  C *Don't Waste Our Water* has ideas for farmers, ranchers, and city governments.

  D It's time to make some changes.

4 What makes saving water especially important to farmers and ranchers?

  F It rains less often on farms and ranches.

  G They need water to make crops grow and for animals to drink.

  H They count on water from rivers, and these sometimes dry up.

  J It is hot on farms and ranches, so people get thirsty.

5 Think of ways to save water that are not listed in the selection. Describe at least one thing you can do that will save water.

_____

_____

_____

_____

_____

_____

_____

Read the selection. Then answer the questions that follow.

Mysterious Moon

On a clear, moonlit night, we can see the face of the "Man in the Moon." Even without a telescope, we see shadows and shapes, bright areas and darker ones. Of course, there is not really a man up there, but if we use our imaginations, it isn't hard to find the outline of a face.

For thousands of years, people wondered about those shadows and shapes. Now we no longer wonder, for people have visited the moon—taken photos, collected rocks and dust. Cameras and robots have explored the moon, answering questions that puzzled astronomers for centuries.

The light areas on the moon are called *terrae* (TEHR ee), which means "lands" in Latin. We now know that these areas are mountainous. Some of the moon's mountain ranges are as high as the Earth's Himalayas.

Long ago, the darker parts of the moon were thought to be oceans. They were named *maria* (MAHR ee ah), the Latin word for "oceans." We have since learned that these areas are covered with dark rock. Ages ago, volcanoes poured lava over the moon's surface. The lava cooled and became hard, leaving dark, smooth rock. Seen from Earth, it looks a bit like water.

Both light and dark areas are dotted with craters. Most of these were formed when meteors and other objects struck the moon, a long time ago. Once in a while, meteors still strike the moon, and they still form craters. Incredibly, astronomers have seen it happen.

Don't feel sad if, the next time you look up at the moon, you see mountains and rock instead of a man's face. Think of the amazing science that brought us our knowledge. Think of the *real* "Man on the Moon"—Neil Armstrong—who walked on its surface in 1969.

Turn the page.

Answer the questions below.

1 What happened on the moon to create dark areas?

   A Mountains rose up, casting shadows on some parts.

   B Volcanoes erupted and poured out lava.

   C People visited the moon, bringing dark dust from the Earth.

   D Comets struck the moon and started fires.

2 What caused the craters on the Moon's surface?

   F Ancient oceans dried up.

   G Meteors collided with the moon.

   H Volcanoes exploded and left great holes.

   J Earthquakes opened up cracks in the moon.

3 Which of the following sentences states both a fact and an opinion?

   A Some of the moon's ranges are as high as the Earth's Himalayas.

   B Long ago, the darker parts of the moon were thought to be oceans.

   C Both light and dark areas are dotted with craters.

   D Incredibly, astronomers have seen it happen.

4 Why are the dark areas on the moon called *maria?*

_____

_____

_____

_____

_____

5 Why does the phrase "the Man in the Moon" have two meanings? Explain both meanings.

_____

_____

_____

_____

_____

Read the selection. Then answer the questions that follow.

Zoo Trip

My little cousin, Sam, was excited because my mom and I were taking him on his first trip to the zoo. We started early Saturday on a beautiful two-hour drive along the ocean.

Our first stop was the reptile house where we saw snakes, lizards, crocodiles, alligators, and turtles. The alligators frightened Sam because of their enormous jaws and sharp teeth.

The next stop was the aquarium, with huge tanks and only a long glass window between us and the fish. Sam jumped because the big shark with its huge mouth seemed so close when it swam to the window.

After a good lunch we visited the wild cat park. The tiger, the largest member of the cat family, looked huge, powerful, and fierce. Three tiger cubs that were sleeping looked soft and warm and reminded Sam of his own kitten. Mom laughed, "Remember, Sam, they grow up to be big tigers."

Sam smiled. "I'm glad my cat won't get that big."

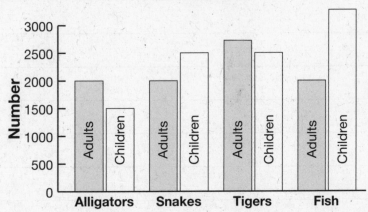

Animals That Children and Adults Liked Best
January

Turn the page.

- -

Answer the questions below.

1 **Which of the following is a statement of fact?**

A My little cousin, Sam, was excited.

B My mom and I were taking him on his first trip to the zoo.

C We started early Saturday on a beautiful two-hour drive.

D The tiger looked huge, powerful, and fierce.

2 **Which sentence is a statement of opinion?**

F Alligators are the most frightening kind of animal.

G The next stop was the aquarium.

H The tiger is the largest member of the cat family.

J Three tiger cubs reminded Sam of his own kitten.

3 **Look at the bar graph. Which animal did children like best in January?**

A alligators

B snakes

C tigers

D fish

4 **Is this story mostly made up of statements of fact or statements of opinion?**

_____

_____

_____

_____

_____

_____

_____

_____

_____

_____

_____

Read the selection. Then answer the questions that follow.

Bird Watching

My best friend, Carlos, and I wanted to go bird watching. We went to the Nature Center at the nearby forest reserve, where we picked up a trail map and a book with many drawings and photographs of various birds in the area. The park ranger talked to us about hiking in the woods and told us about birds we might see.

"You boys have fun. Follow the trail and keep your eyes open."

We gathered the necessary items: a forest service map, two bottles of water, snacks, a compass for direction, and a whistle for emergencies.

Two weeks ago, on a beautiful, sunny day, we set out for our destination, Brown Lake, which was two miles away. I led the way up a narrow trail through a thick forest.

We turned north, crossed a creek, climbed a steep hill, and headed east along a high ridge. I spotted some beautiful little birds flying among the low bushes.

Suddenly I heard the sharp sound of a whistle. I quickly turned back, fearful of what I might find, and ran toward Carlos, who was kneeling next to a wounded bird that was lying on the ground. It was breathing hard, and its wing appeared to be broken.

Carlos was almost in tears, and I was shaking with fright, but we kept our cool and did not panic. I carefully picked up the bird, wrapping it in my sweater, and held it gently as we hurried back to the Center. We were relieved that the bird was still alive.

Yesterday we heard from the ranger that the bird had recovered and was ready to be released. We went to the Center and showed our map to the ranger, pointing out where we had found the bird. We had no doubt the bird would find its way home.

Turn the page.

Answer the questions below.

1 Which of the following is a statement of opinion?

   A We gathered the necessary items.

   B Two weeks ago, we set out for our destination.

   C I ran back toward Carlos.

   D I spotted some beautiful little birds.

2 Which of the following most accurately describes the story?

   F It contains mostly statements of fact.

   G It contains mostly statements of opinion.

   H All of its statements are facts.

   J All of its statements are opinions.

3 The author writes, "We had no doubt the bird would find its way home." Which of the following best describes that statement?

   A It is a statement of fact.

   B It is a statement of opinion.

   C It is a statement of fact and opinion.

   D It is not a true statement.

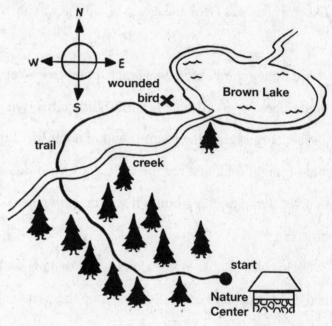

4 Look at the map. Where did the boys find the wounded bird?

   F not far from Brown Lake

   G among the trees

   H between the Nature Center and the creek

   J close to where the trail crossed the creek

5 Write one statement of fact about Carlos.

_____

_____

_____

_____

_____

_____

Read the selection. Then answer the questions that follow.

Snowball

In 2003 the zoo in my city bought a male white Bengal tiger. His name is Snowball, and he was born in a wildlife park somewhere in the United States. His ancestors were from forests in central India. At the age of seven months, he traveled by airplane to our zoo. Now he is two years old and will probably live another twenty years.

There are only 133 captive white Bengal tigers in the world. These great beasts are beautiful creatures with blue eyes, a pink nose, and creamy white fur covered with chocolate-colored stripes. They are as tall as a fourth grader, twice as long, and five times heavier, with a tail that measures three to four feet. They are good swimmers but poor climbers, slow runners but stealthy and accomplished hunters. When hungry or sick, they have been known to attack and kill people.

Over the years greedy hunters have killed and sold these animals for large amounts of money. Population growth has destroyed much of the forests and grasslands where they live, and today no white tigers remain in the wild. These rare animals can now be seen only in zoos or wildlife parks.

Bengal tigers are solitary animals. Snowball seems happy in his home, a one-acre hilly park closed in by a high chain-link fence, with trees, a pond, and a dark cave. He spends his day walking, lying in the sun, playing with his toys, sleeping, sharpening his claws, and stalking the water buffalo in a nearby enclosure. In the late afternoon, the keepers feed Snowball three whole chickens, ten pounds of meat, ground bone, and vitamins. He then sleeps in his night house until morning, when he begins his day by splashing in the pond.

It is a shame not all Bengal tigers were as fortunate as Snowball.

Turn the page.

Answer the questions below.

1 Which of the following is a statement of opinion?

  A Snowball was born in a wildlife park somewhere in the United States.

  B Greedy hunters have killed and sold these animals.

  C Bengal tigers are solitary animals.

  D In the late afternoon, the keepers feed Snowball.

2 What would be the best way to find out if there are only 133 captive white Bengal tigers in the world?

  F Ask someone at school.

  G Check on the Internet.

  H Go to the zoo and ask someone.

  J Read a book about India.

3 What does the picture of Snowball tell you about him?

  A He is chasing a ball.

  B He is sharpening his claws

  C He is a playful animal.

  D He is a small animal.

4 Based on the selection, write a statement about Snowball that includes two opinions.

_____

_____

_____

_____

5 Write two statements of fact about why so few white Bengal tigers still exist.

_____

_____

_____

_____

Read the selection. Then answer the questions that follow.

Uncle Boo and Wags

Uncle Boo lived alone, so I usually stopped to visit on my way home from school. Back in March I noticed that he'd gotten kind of depressed. He hardly ever laughed anymore, and he'd even stopped telling tall tales about his days in the Navy. I missed hearing about the faraway ports he'd visited, and thought a lot about what I could do to cheer him up.

Finally I had an idea, and I phoned Uncle Boo.

"Since Mom has a new job, Wags is alone all day," I told him, "and I don't think it's good for him. Do you have any ideas?"

Uncle Boo didn't answer immediately, but then he said slowly, "Why not bring him here on your way to school? I can keep an eye on him."

After school I found Uncle Boo smiling and patting Wags.

"Your dog is a great companion," he said. "We had a fine time at the park. Can you stay awhile? I'll tell you about my trip to China."

Turn the page.

Answer the questions below.

1   **What is the main point of this story?**

A   It is good to laugh and tell tales.

B   Old men and young boys make good friends.

C   Caring about others means helping them.

D   It is important to have a dog.

2   **Which of the following is not a theme of the story?**

F   It is good to have company.

G   Dogs should not be left alone.

H   It is important to make others happy.

J   Everyone needs someone.

3   **Which sentence is most important in helping you know what the theme is?**

A   Uncle Boo lived alone.

B   I thought a lot about how to cheer him up.

C   I don't think it's good for him.

D   Uncle Boo didn't answer immediately.

4   **In the first paragraph, how did the author show how the child felt about his uncle?**

_____

_____

_____

_____

_____

_____

_____

_____

_____

_____

_____

Read the selection. Then answer the questions that follow.

The Whale Shark

My dad is a scientist who studies animals that live in oceans. He often dives deep beneath the sea and swims among the fish. He wears a wet suit to keep warm, fins on his feet to move quickly through the water, a mask so he can see clearly, and a snorkel for breathing.

Last week he called from the South Pacific where he was working with some college students who were studying fish and plant life in the oceans.

"Guess what we saw today. We swam close to the ocean's biggest fish, the whale shark."

It sounded pretty frightening to me because these huge fish can grow to a length of almost fifty feet. I am in the fourth grade, so that fish is about ten times as big as I am. Dad told the students that it is important to be respectful of all animal life. It is necessary to learn an animal's habits, how it behaves, and what it fears. Dad also warned against touching or trying to ride the animals.

The whale shark is a peaceful, friendly, slow swimmer that travels alone. If frightened, startled, or excited, it might flip its tail and knock a swimmer or small boat out of the water.

One of his students, interviewed by a local TV reporter, said, "This shark was just so gentle. He swam around in large circles, rubbing his back against the boats and sometimes bumping into a swimmer. He was only an arm's length away, and he didn't seem bothered at all. I wanted to touch him, but I knew that was a bad idea. After all, in a way we were guests in his home."

I guess if we are kind to the large creatures of the sea, they will be kind to us.

Turn the page.

Answer the questions below.

1 Which sentence best states the theme of the story?

  A These huge fish can grow to a length of almost fifty feet.

  B It is important to be respectful of all animal life.

  C The whale shark is a peaceful, friendly, slow swimmer.

  D After all, in a way we were guests in his home.

2 Which of the following is not a theme of this story?

  F A huge number of animals live beneath the sea.

  G We learn by studying animals in the places where they live.

  H It is important not to touch or try to ride wild animals.

  J Scientists learn by swimming with fish.

3 What was the author's main reason for writing this story?

  A to entertain the reader in the habits of the whale shark

  B to persuade the reader to stay away from wild animals

  C to express feelings about the natural world and the whale shark

  D to inform the reader about the habits of wild animals

4 Why did the student not touch the whale shark?

  F The student was afraid of the shark.

  G The shark was too far away.

  H The student was being respectful of the shark.

  J The shark did not like to be touched.

5 What facts about the whale shark are important to the theme of the selection?

_____

_____

_____

_____

_____

_____

_____

_____

Read the selection. Then answer the questions that follow.

Watch Out

My brother, Joe, and I are fortunate to live next to a vast forest reserve with tall trees, a stream, giant boulders, hills to climb, and a huge pond where we can fish. We are allowed to go exploring as long as we promise to be cautious, stay together, and not stray too far from the path. However, we get tired of Mom telling us to pay attention and watch where we go. Joe is a fifth grader, I'm in the fourth grade, and we believe we can take care of ourselves.

Yesterday we asked if we could go catch butterflies in the woods. Mom said, "Fine, but be back for lunch. And Sarah, please watch out and don't be reckless. Try not to get so bruised and scratched." Joe grinned because he seldom gets hurt.

We love to be in the woods, where the long branches of the trees form a green ceiling. After climbing a steep hill, we came to a large meadow filled with colorful wildflowers. Immediately Joe caught two butterflies. I was having no luck at all until I looked down a little valley, where I saw hundreds of them.

Off I flew and suddenly slipped, falling and rolling down the hill. Joe came running toward me yelling, "I'll help you."

"Watch out, Joe, it's really slippery." He tripped on a big rock, flew into the air, and crashed into a giant log. He slowly picked himself up. I was scared. Joe had a big bump on his head.

"You hurt yourself and Mom will be mad," I whimpered.

"Yes, but it's your fault. You were reckless as usual, and I was only trying to rescue you."

I put my arm around him and we trudged home.

"I'm sorry, Joe. From now on I will listen to Mom."

Turn the page.

Answer the questions below.

1 What did the author want us to learn from this story?

  A that children should not run too fast

  B that parents have reasons for what they say

  C that the great outdoors can be dangerous

  D that these children were lucky to live near a forest

2 What is one reason that Sarah slipped and fell?

  F She loved being in the woods.

  G She saw a meadow full of wildflowers.

  H She was tired of being told to pay attention.

  J She was hurrying to be back in time for lunch.

3 Which of the following is one of the themes of the story?

  A Boys are more careful than girls.

  B It is hard to catch butterflies.

  C It is important to help others.

  D A mistake can hurt someone else.

4 Why is the story called "Watch Out"?

_____

_____

_____

_____

_____

5 What sentences in the first paragraph tell you that Sarah may be going to learn a lesson?

_____

_____

_____

_____

_____

Read the selection. Then answer the questions that follow.

Teamwork

Last month our teacher assigned a history project. "You have two weeks to write a three-page report on the Civil War, and you may choose to work alone or in teams."

I smiled at my best friend, Jan, who is really smart, and said, "Let's work together."

"No, Lisa, I want to do this by myself."

That surprised me because we always do everything together. My grades are not great, but I am a good artist, and pictures can improve a report and make it more interesting.

So I asked Andy and Mark, who are also very bright, to work with me.

The three of us enjoyed studying together. I noticed Jan looking at us in a funny way when she saw us smiling and whispering over books at the library.

Our team earned an A, but Jan got a B. When I had lunch with her the next day she said, "Next time let's all be a team, because four heads are even better than one."

Civil War Project Grades

	A	B	C	D
7 Team Reports (21 students)	2 (6)	3 (9)	2 (6)	0 (0)
6 Individual Reports (6 students)	0 (0)	2 (2)	3 (3)	1 (1)

© Pearson Education 4

Turn the page.

Answer the questions below.

1 Which generalization can you make from the facts in the selection?

A It is fun to work with others.

B It is smart to work alone.

C Many minds are better than one.

D To get something done well, do it yourself.

2 Which of the following is a valid generalization?

F Pictures always improve a report.

G Jan always wants to work alone.

H Team members always have a good time.

J Team members need to work together.

3 What generalization can you make based on the chart?

A More students in teams earned the two best grades.

B Most students in teams spent more time studying.

C Most of the students worked alone rather than in teams.

D More students who worked alone got the two worst grades.

4 What is one generalization that appears in the story. What clue word makes it a generalization?

_____

_____

_____

_____

_____

_____

_____

_____

_____

_____

Read the selection. Then answer the questions that follow.

Endless Energy

More and more people are thinking about how to get energy from sources other than oil, coal, or gas. Those fuels are generally dirty, and one day they will run out. *Renewable* energy means energy that will always be there (renewable = that can be made new again). The wind keeps blowing, the sun keeps shining, and the Earth keeps heating underground rocks. So as long as the Earth is here, those forms of energy will be here.

People have been using wind power for a long time. Before engines were invented, ships had sails that filled with wind, moving them across the water. In some parts of the world, small sailing boats are still used for fishing.

In the past, people generally built windmills to grind grain and to pump water. A windmill has sails that turn as they catch the wind. The sails turn a shaft that runs a pump or grinder. Today there are large modern windmills that work together in wind farms to produce electricity.

Sunlight can also be used to make electricity. The sun shines on cells, which are often placed on the roof of a house or building. When the sun hits these cells, there is a reaction that makes electricity. As costs for electricity rise, more people are beginning to use energy from the sun.

Geothermal energy is a way of using underground water that has been heated by rocks, which have themselves been heated by the great temperature of the Earth's core. This hot water is turned into steam, which then runs a machine that makes electricity.

Using renewable energy is a good way to meet the electricity needs of the growing number of people in the world.

Turn the page.

Answer the questions below.

1 Which generalization about renewable energy is made by the author?

A These forms of energy will always be there.

B In many parts of the world, wind is used to run motors.

C Few people know about renewable energy.

D Solar energy is generally cleaner than wind energy.

2 Which of the following is not a valid generalization?

F Sunlight can be used to create electricity.

G Wind power can be used to grind grain.

H Sources of coal will never run out.

J Underground hot water creates steam.

3 A hundred years ago wind power was generally used to

A run automobiles.

B pump water.

C warm houses.

D pump oil.

4 The picture shows a use of

F geothermal energy.

G sun power.

H wind power.

J oil and gas.

5 Make two generalizations about why finding sources of energy is becoming a problem in the world.

_____

_____

_____

_____

_____

_____

_____

Read the selection. Then answer the questions that follow.

The Gorilla

We know this great creature from zoos, books, and movies. It is the largest member of a group of animals that includes monkeys, chimpanzees, and orangutans. An adult male gorilla can weigh from three hundred to four hundred pounds. The gorilla's body is covered with thick, dark hair except for its face, upper chest, fingers, palms, and the soles of its feet. Its powerful jaws have big teeth for tearing and grinding food. Its arms are long and very strong. An adult male gorilla could win a tug of war with six men.

Gorillas look a lot like people, with two arms and two legs and similar hands and feet, but they walk on both their arms and legs, using the backs of the fingers like a foot. The head and body look almost human.

Gorillas are found in only three forests of Africa, two in the lowlands and the third in the mountains. Each day a gorilla eats nearly forty pounds of leaves, twigs, bark, and grass. It gets moisture from the juicy plants and so drinks little water. Once in a while it will munch on a bird's egg or an insect. Except for a nap at noon, it eats from morning until night.

The main social group for gorillas is the family. The oldest male is the leader and is responsible for the females with babies and the young males and females. Family life is generally peaceful, kind, and considerate, with little fighting. The leader protects the family and guides the group in the forest, which it shares with other families.

Today the gorilla is in danger. Forests are getting smaller because of the cutting of trees, clearing of forests for homes, and grazing of cattle. In addition, hunters kill the gorilla for food. Without the protection of these forests in Africa, this peaceful animal will disappear.

Turn the page.

Answer the questions below.

1 Which of the following generalizations is valid?

A Gorillas are in danger because forests are being destroyed.

B The number of gorillas in the wild is increasing every year.

C Human hunters are the only threat to the survival of the gorilla.

D The greatest danger to gorilla families is other gorilla families.

2 What generalization can you make about the gorilla's diet?

F Gorillas eat only plants.

G The gorilla's main food is insects and bird's eggs.

H Gorillas get most of their moisture from plants.

J Gorillas eat most of their food at night.

3 How does a gorilla spend most of its day?

A sleeping in caves

B playing with other gorillas

C napping and playing

D looking for food

4 What generalization can you make based on the picture of a gorilla?

_____

_____

_____

_____

_____

5 What generalization can you make about a gorilla's family life?

_____

_____

_____

_____

_____

Read the selection. Then answer the questions that follow.

Chelsea's Choice

Chelsea is a busy fourth grader who does very well in school and participates in many after-school activities. She's the captain of the soccer team, a volunteer at the city library, she babysits, and she takes piano lessons.

Recently she tried out for the school play and was given the leading role, which was great news, but it meant she now had to rearrange her schedule. Rehearsals were planned for Tuesday and Thursday between 3:00 P.M. and 5:00 P.M.

It was a problem. Soccer was her favorite sport, and Chelsea's teammates relied on her. She felt it was important to assist at the library. She cared about the Lopez children she babysat for and liked earning money. Also, she enjoyed studying the piano and could now play "New York, New York." So her big challenge was to determine how she could do it all.

Chelsea's Schedule			
3:00 P.M.	4:00 P.M.	5:00 P.M.	6:00 P.M.
Monday	Soccer ← →		
Tuesday		Babysitting ← →	
Wednesday	Piano Lesson ← →	Soccer ← →	
Thursday	Library ← →	Babysitting ← →	
Friday	Soccer ← →		

Turn the page.

Answer the questions below.

1 Which activities will Chelsea not have to change?

  A piano lesson and soccer

  B soccer and babysitting

  C babysitting and library

  D library and piano lesson

2 On which day does Chelsea have the most free time?

  F Monday

  G Tuesday

  H Thursday

  J Friday

3 Which of the following sentences from the story is a statement of opinion?

  A She's the captain of the soccer team.

  B Recently she tried out for the school play.

  C Rehearsals were planned for Tuesday and Thursday.

  D Chelsea's teammates relied on her.

4 Which activities will Chelsea need to give up or reschedule?

Read the selection. Then answer the questions that follow.

Wagon Train

The Oregon Trail was the route—or routes—used by thousands of settlers from the 1840s through the mid-1860s to reach the territory along the West Coast of North America. They made this challenging and dangerous two-thousand-mile trip in wagon trains, some made up of as many as twenty covered wagons. Most left from Independence, Missouri, in the spring when the winter snow had melted. Many kept a record of their five- to six-month odyssey. The following may have come from the diary of a young member of a pioneer family in 1865.

May 1. We left Independence a month ago and are making good time, traveling more than 15 miles per day. Today we crossed the Platte River after the men spent several days building rafts to float the people and wagons across.

June 20. We arrived in Fort Laramie after many weeks of slow and arduous travel through the Great Plains. Because of blinding dust storms followed by terrible thunderstorms, we only went a few miles a day. We need to rest here for a few days before attempting to cross the Rocky Mountains.

August 25. We finally reached Fort Hall and everyone is exhausted. Crossing the mountains was a struggle. We borrowed one another's oxen to pull the wagons up the steep trail, but going down was trickier. To keep the wagons from slipping away, the men held on to them from behind with long ropes.

October 1. Since leaving Fort Hall, we have followed the beautiful Columbia River all the way to Oregon City. It's been six months of unbelievable adventure.

Turn the page.

Answer the questions below.

1 Where did the wagon train run into dust storms?

   A near the Mississippi River

   B on the plains along the Platte River

   C near the Rocky Mountains

   D along the Columbia River

2 Using the scale, what is the distance from Fort Kearny to Fort Laramie?

   F 150 miles

   G 150 kilometers

   H 300 miles

   J 600 miles

3 Where were the settlers during most of their journey?

   A in mountains

   B on the Great Plains

   C close to rivers

   D near forts

4 The author writes, "Since leaving Fort Hall, we have followed the beautiful Columbia River all the way to Oregon City." Which of the following best describes this statement?

   F It is a statement of opinion.

   G It contains statements of both fact and opinion.

   H It is a statement of fact.

   J It is not a true statement.

5 Using the map, describe the route from Fort Hall to Oregon City.

_____

_____

_____

_____

_____

_____

_____

Read the selection. Then answer the questions that follow.

The Potato

The potato is a vegetable, something called a *tuber,* which is the fat underground stem of certain plants. It is easy to grow and filled with the fiber, minerals, and protein people need in order to stay healthy. It also contains most of the vitamins needed for sustenance.

The potato was first grown in the cold, tall Andes Mountains of South America at least five thousand years ago, but it was not until the time of Columbus, when explorers brought the potato to Europe, that the rest of the world learned about this food.

At first, the potato was eaten only by farm animals and very poor people because of prejudice against it. The potato is a member of the nightshade family of plants (as is the tomato), and the leaves, in fact, are poisonous.

Then, in the 1700s, a Frenchman ate potatoes for the first time while a prisoner of war in Germany. Thanks to him, the potato gained widespread popularity.

When the potato was brought to Ireland, it became the primary food of the poor farmers of that cold country. Then, in the 1840s, a potato disease destroyed crops throughout Europe. Over a four-year period, nearly a million people starved to death in Ireland, and between 1847 and 1854 more than a million and a half people left Ireland and came to America.

Potatoes can be used in many different ways—baked, boiled, fried, in a stew, or mashed. No matter how they are prepared, they taste good and are healthful.

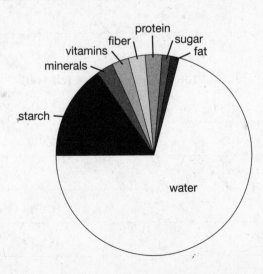

Turn the page.

Answer the questions below.

1 The potato is mostly made up of

   A fat and sugar.

   B water.

   C starch.

   D vitamins and minerals.

2 What would be the best title for the circle graph of the potato?

   F The Potato

   G Food Value of the Potato

   H What to Look for in the Potato

   J History of the Potato

3 Which sentence best describes this selection?

   A It contains only statements of fact.

   B It contains only statements of opinion.

   C It contains mostly statements of fact.

   D It contains more statements of opinion than statements of fact.

4 What additional graphic do you think would be helpful to include with this selection?

_____

_____

_____

_____

_____

5 What did you learn from the circle graph that the passage did not tell you?

_____

_____

_____

_____

_____